Prepare Yourself, Your Client, and Your Practice for Ketamine Assisted Psychotherapy

Karen L. Smith MSS, LCSW

Preface

The main body of this book is loaded with introductory material, so I will limit repetition here. I have a handful of language-use choices I will note as well as highlight a set of professional perspective themes.

Patient/Client/Participant: I have made varying decisions over my career about what I call people who work with me. These days it is client. Totally interesting possible discussion, but not relevant to this book. In this book, when I refer to patients, I am making a reference to a medical aspect of the work, for instance when patients work with infusion centers. When I am referencing outpatient psychotherapy, I use the word client. When I am referencing psychedelic journeys that may not inherently have a psychotherapy component, I use the word participant.

Folx: Folks is a favorite way of referencing people for me, even in professional settings. I switched to folx a couple years ago in a bid for gender inclusivity. While folks isn't gender specific at all, which is in part why I always loved it, the x just adds that little extra welcome.

Indigenous Medicines: Ketamine is not a psychedelic with a long history, but the use of psychedelic journeys for purposes of healing are richly embedded into many indigenous populations across the globe. Much of the current frame for working with psychedelics is built on the knowledge, traditions, and current indigenous leadership in the field. In a commitment to staying in my lane, I am unable to offer any of this knowledge or background from an authentic place of knowing. There are others who have already done so beautifully and who will continue to provide this leadership.

Social Work Perspective: While writing this book, I noticed what seemed like way too many moments that explain why I do certain things for free, or why I want protocols that decrease the financial insurmountability of this treatment for most people. I will just say it; I am a social worker. I like to make money, but I have other things that are important to me too. You are free to ignore all my bids for economic justice and arguments that we should provide public education, but I did not feel free to leave those bids out.

Documents in Resources Section: In service of providing practical help to the clinician interested in ketamine-assisted psychotherapy, when I mention having a client fill out an intake form, or sending some psycho-education to the client about ketamine, or reviewing consent documents with a client, those resources are included in the resource section, with downloadable version on my website's Clinical Resources.*

It is my great wish that this is a helpful collection of information, or at least enough to get you started in what could be an very exciting addition to your clinical work.

---

* https://fullliving.com/clinical-resources/

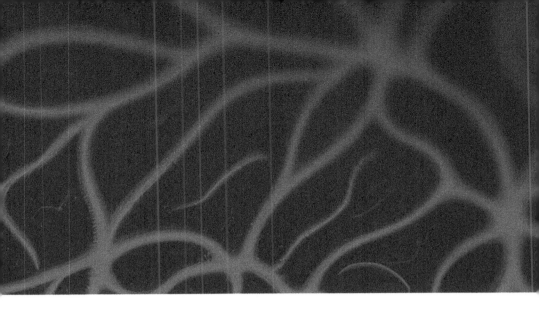

To my boy, Jack,

The opportunity to engage and dance and wrestle with your emerging self has been the journey of a lifetime. You have stretched and grown my heart, mind, capacity, skills and spirit.

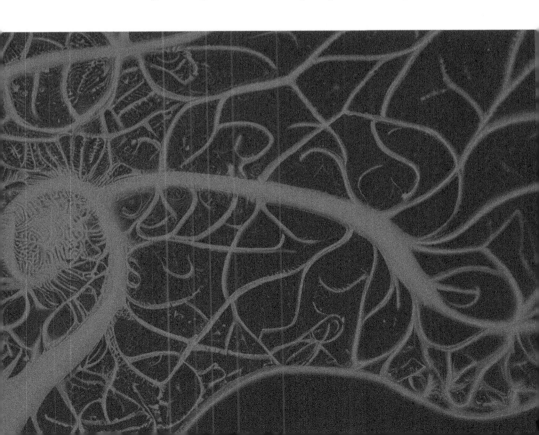

Contents

What Are Ketamine and KAP?

Psychedelics and psychedelic-assisted psychotherapies have recently resurfaced in the national consciousness. The current conversation is driven in large part by the active FDA studies with MDMA (ecstasy/molly) and psilocybin (mushrooms), many of which are now in final-stage trials for treatment of a range of disorders and conditions. Leading medical and research facilities are studying use of multiple psychedelic medicines and the psychotherapy-assisted psychedelic experience to help relieve symptoms of depression, post-traumatic stress disorder, addictions, and obsessive compulsive disorders. New studies emerge monthly exploring how these medicines can help alleviate suffering for people with a range of diagnoses and conditions. Both MDMA and psilocybin are slated for legal use by trained psychotherapists in the next few years.

As exciting as it is to imagine these tools becoming available to our clients, there is already an available, legal, underutilized, and seriously brilliant medicine: ketamine. Ketamine is currently prescribed for off-label use for several mental health diagnoses including depression and anxiety. Even when MDMA and psilocybin are available, as a clinician, I would be unlikely to shift to their use with clients, and I hope this book will help explain why.

Ketamine is a medicine particularly well suited for use in psychedelic-assisted psychotherapy. Its unique features fit well within the psychotherapy frame. Besides being a particularly psychotherapy-friendly medicine, it has features that can make it significantly less costly than the other psychedelic options for our clients.

I hope to offer enough of an overview of ketamine and ketamine-assisted psychotherapy (KAP) for readers to have both a sense of its value to your practice, and realistic expectations of the nuts and bolts of tooling yourself, your clients, and your practice for KAP. For every client you have had who is/was seriously stuck, ketamine is a tool worth your consideration.

WHAT IS KETAMINE?

Ketamine is a prescription medicine used commonly as a dissociative anesthetic. It has been routinely and safely used in hospitals and outpatient medical facilities for over five decades. Its primary use has been to facilitate minor surgeries and procedures with patients as young as newborns to the elderly. Compared to other anesthetics, it is significantly safer, has few counter-indications, and has minimal potential negative side effects, making it preferred for short procedures.

Recently, it has been increasingly used as an off-label medication for treatment-resistant depression. Unlike traditional antidepressants, the medicine impacts the glutamate system to produce a decrease in depressive symptoms. Two-thirds of patients with treatment-resistant depression who failed to see improvement on two other antidepressants see an improvement of their symptoms when taking ketamine as a protocol-specific medicine, separate from participation in psychotherapy.

The medicine's administration can take multiple forms: infusion, intramuscular injections, nasal spray, or two types of dissolvable tablets. Most outpatient psychotherapists have their clients get prescriptions for tablets, as most of us are not medical professionals and are unable to participate in administering the medicine. Tablets also allow clients the option of at-home use.

Ketamine as a Psychedelic

The molecule-induced reduction of depression symptoms is unique to ketamine. But like its psychedelic cousins, ketamine is also used for the psychedelic experience it produces, which can lead to invaluable insights and experiences our clients can use to understand themselves and find a new path out of their suffering.

The psychedelic experience can help folx with a range of diagnoses, but clinicians also use the medicine's psychedelic properties to work with our clients around trauma, grief, letting go, opening up, gaining a new perspective, or having a new somatic experience. (Note that clients must present symptoms of depression or anxiety to be eligible for a prescription).

As "dissociative anesthetic" isn't a great description of what ketamine offers the client in the psychedelic experience, here are some hopefully more user-friendly descriptions:

- One of the anesthetic effects of the medicine is that it alters external sensory input. Sounds in the space around the person on the journey are often muted or differently experienced. The sounds may weave their way into their unconscious, and if desired, clients can tune in to them, but they can commonly also tune them out. This supports clients toward a uniquely internal focus—perfect for work on themselves. To reduce external stimulation, ketamine clients typically wear eye masks and lie down during the session.

- The dissociative experience can play out like having two selves during the medicine session—the dreamer and the observing ego. One is having a wild experience, while the other is quite self-aware and able to offer direction, reassurance, and containment to the "tripping" self.

- While a ketamine experience offers the mental mind-bending characteristics of classic psychedelics, it does so in an affective, emotionally rich environment. During the medicine session, clients are not just having interesting thoughts; the anesthetic properties are providing them within an embodied, somatic experience.

Ketamine for Psychotherapy

Ketamine has several unique features that make it particularly well-suited for outpatient psychotherapy models of treatment.

- The ketamine medicine session, or trip, only lasts about 40 minutes. The shortness of this experience allows for a very focused intention for each session, as opposed to other types of psychedelic sessions, which can last for hours and therefore usually cover a lot of internal territory. The brevity of the ketamine session additionally makes it more financially feasible to have a therapist present.

- It is legal for use. While the details surrounding credentialing and diagnostic criteria for off-label use are unsettled and murky, ketamine is already legal for off-label use in therapeutic contexts, with malpractice insurance options for licensed clinicians.

- Minimal side effects or post-session emotional crash. This is relevant when compared to other psychedelics, like MDMA and psilocybin, which also have minimal side effects, except both can sometimes lead to massive emotional hangovers.

- Dosing is not one-size-fits-all. Ketamine allows the clinician/prescriber/client to have more influence over how the tool is used in any particular session. There are multiple versions of a medicine experience that a client can use to do their psychotherapy work.

  » At a low dose, clients have a psychelytic effect, which produces psychic flexibility, allowing clients to have a talk therapy session freer of default-mode processing, with easier access to associative and unconscious material, and lowered defenses, allowing them to discuss old topics with new impressions.

» At a medium dose, clients can have a psychedelic experience. This can provide them with new material; symbolic exploration about their most stuck places; and embodied, somatic experiences of some of their truths. It is an opportunity for new perspectives.

» At high doses, many clients have experiences of mystical revelation and ego dissolution. While hardly a place to start, for some clients, these experiences will be some of the most meaningful of their lives.

Ketamine Has an Image Problem

I suppose I can't end a section titled "What Is Ketamine?" without mentioning horse tranquilizers and Special K. It is true that ketamine is used as a tranquilizer, which is another way to refer to anesthetics. Obviously, the amount of ketamine it takes to dose a horse for surgery is significantly higher than it takes to set a ten-year-old's broken arm in the ER, but it is essentially the same medicine, same concept.

Special K is one of the names of a street drug version of ketamine, typically snorted and at a lower dose than used for medicine sessions. In the 1980s, and in increasing numbers again today, it seems to be primarily used as a social drug, strongly identified with the club/music/dance/festival scene. Ketamine's street-drug status is a contributor to ketamine's stigma.

Some psychedelics overcome the street-drug public-perception problem with an idealized allure of "plant medicine." In this psychedelic renaissance, there is a celebration of nature and the natural world, the old ways, indigenous and native traditions with various medicines, coining the current term plant medicine. It is a lovely concept, and very appropriate to a couple of the medicines healers and scientists are currently using and studying. Ketamine doesn't benefit from a back-to-nature narrative.

Stigmas and allures aside, the qualities ketamine offers the mind/soma/spirit of the client are beautifully aligned with the specific help we need as psychotherapists with our very stuck clients.

WHAT IS KETAMINE-ASSISTED PSYCHOTHERAPY (KAP)?

Many devotees of exploring altered consciousness, and many who have simply experimented with psychedelics at some point in their lives, have had psychedelic experiences they were able to use to change their lives. Psychedelic-assisted psychotherapies are trying to improve the chances of a similar outcome. KAP activities are oriented toward:

- Activating/harnessing/capitalizing on the power/possibility of the medicine

- Facilitating a dialogue between the client's unconscious and conscious selves, connecting to their inner healing wisdom

- Helping our clients use agency and intentionality to prepare their conscious and unconscious selves for the psychedelic experience

- Increasing the possibility of the psychedelic experience directly addressing the content/themes that are the focus of the client's work

- Supporting our clients taking ownership over integrating the experience to make proper therapeutic use of their journeys

The specifics about how practitioners operationalize KAP vary widely. KAP can be part of a weekend retreat, a series of outpatient treatments, or a supportive service offered to ketamine-infusion patients. KAP can even be limited to a therapist helping with the preparation and integration sessions on either side of the medicine session that the client does at home or with another KAP practitioner.

The common denominator in the hands of a skilled clinician is that the medicine isn't the main event: the therapy is. Ketamine is just a tool. The vehicles for central change are the psychotherapy and the client's inner healer. So what is KAP? It is just psychotherapy, with the assistance of short, psychedelic experiences, which aid in the discovery of key internal data and revealing somatic experiences.

In later sections of this book, I offer more details about each issue covered below, but here is an overview of some elements of KAP to help you conceptualize the work.

The Medicine Session

The topography of KAP work places the medicine session in the center. We do the bulk of the psychotherapeutic heavy lifting in the sessions before the medicine session, helping the client prepare for their medicine journey, and after the medicine session, helping them integrate the experience. But the medicine session is still the crown jewel—the experience we hope will offer our client an opportunity for psychic transformation.

The medicine session allows for lucid contact with unconscious material. If your client has themes they are working on, places they feel stuck or confused, questions they have for their unconscious, difficulty formulating a new narrative or perspective, the medicine session is an opportunity for therapeutic exploration. During the psychedelic journey, clients have lowered defenses and fluid neural pathways that can provide new, original thoughts not burdened by default-mode processing of material.

Clients sometimes have what they describe as mystical/spiritual experiences that give them a radically different perspective on themselves, others, and life itself. Many of us have very narrow world/self/other views that do much to dictate our experience. Psychedelic experiences can open a totally new, expansive understanding.

There are many ways our KAP work might structurally look during the client's medicine session. They might have brought their medicine to our office and self-administered it at the start of the session. We might be with them at an infusion center in a chair next to their lounger. Or we might even be doing the medicine session with them virtually while they do the medicine session at home. In all these scenarios, we may be sitting quietly with them while they lie down with eye shades and music, having an internal experience. Or they might be doing what we call a psychelytic dose, which is lower, where they continue to engage with the therapist in dialogue but with lowered defenses and a flexible mind. Part of learning about how to provide KAP is building a structure that fits with your particular practice and approach to psychotherapy.

There are some overarching principles guiding how to interact with the client during the medicine session and immediately following. The rule of thumb is to be as non-directive as possible. We are relying on our client's state of mind to offer both client and clinician a new, original direction or perspective. Being non-directive frees us of the burden of having to know how to help our client. Both of us are asking their inner healer for help. Relieved of the burden of "fixing" our client, we can focus on the task of non-direction, which is a sufficiently challenging task for many a skilled clinician!

We might only be working with our client on either side of the medicine session, doing preparation and integration work. They might be doing the medicine session at home with a friend, or at an infusion center, or with another KAP provider. Even though we are not present at the medicine session, it is still a central focus of our attention. Our work will be unpacking the material and experience of the medicine session and integrating it into the client's life in relevant ways.

Set

KAP starts well before the medicine session. Regardless of the setting of our work, a prerequisite to medicine sessions is preparation work. In part, this is a concrete, practical checklist, including such items as a thorough evaluation, detailed discussions about how they are going to feel with the medicine, steps to acquire a prescription, what themes or issues or concerns might come up, how they should spend the time immediately following the session and the days after, what their loved ones should expect on the day of treatment, etc. But the more rich preparation is related to mindset.

Clients are best served going into their medicine sessions with a mindset for therapeutic work. Prior to the medicine session, we help them develop a formal "intention" for what they want from themselves/their unconscious/their inner healer/the medicine session experience. Sometimes these are general intentions, like, "I want to trust the process" or "I want to be open to the journey." Sometimes they are more specific, like, "Help me access joy," "I want an experience of self-confidence," or "Who am I beyond my trauma/diagnosis/issue." In KAP, we work with our clients to help them set and hone their intentions before each medicine session.

In my own practice, I help clients start to craft their intention from the first free initial intake/info session I offer. Besides specifically talking to them about developing some clear intentions, I also send them some of the write-ups, included in the resources section, to get their ideas percolating. I ask them to journal about their intentions, have conversations with friends, talk to spiritual directors/advisors, meditate, etc. Setting up the intention solidly in the conscious and unconscious mind prior to the medicine session increases the chance the session will be fruitful.

In addition to an intention, set and mindset are about our clients' treatment of this work. Part of our preparation work is to help them to have a mindset of openness to the process and connection with their inner healing wisdom. KAP is more potent when we and our client treat it as a special, even ceremonial, event. It is important for the session to be in their consciousness in the days and hours before. Given the opportunity ketamine offers the client, we want to help them gather their external and internal focus, their psychic and libidinal energies, and direct it to their intention and mindset.

Setting

Setting refers to the environment of the medicine session. There are various physical locations where a client might have their medicine journey experience.

They may be with us in our outpatient office, at a weekend group retreat setting, or an infusion center. They may also be taking the medicine at home, perhaps as a virtual session with us, perhaps instead limited to a virtual session immediately before and/or immediately after the medicine session, or perhaps the client is doing the session completely self-directed at home with another adult in the home simply for purposes of safety.

Wherever they are, the setting/environment should be optimized for a grounding experience. It needs to be calming, organized, and with minimal distractions. The client is served by feeling good and safe in the place. They need to be equipped with blankets and eye shades, sometimes noise-canceling headphones, sometimes well-curated music as an accompaniment. Prior to the medicine session, you may want to explore with them what other items might help them feel safe and attended to in the space.

They need food and drink and low distraction available immediately following their medicine session, and perhaps a journal on hand or art materials set up to try to reflect on their experience immediately following the journey. They need anyone they have to interact with to know they are in a special mental space. They need to be allowed to take the lead in directing their activities, like whether or not they want to talk or sleep or journal.

If we are present during the medicine session, virtually or live, our KAP work is to maintain a safe and contained setting. Besides concrete offerings, like assistance to the restroom if they need it, an extra blanket, or glass of water, we are protecting their session from intrusion. The point of the good setting is to create a sacred space to do important internal work. We take care of the external environment so they can tune in to their internal landscape.

Integration

While the medicine session is the crown jewel of KAP, integration is the cornerstone. Without it, clients may have a lovely medicine experience, but obviously we have loftier goals. We are aiming for things like the healing of their core and development of a new normal. Whatever rich material the client's ketamine journey brings, its relevance shows up in their ability to use it to change their life.

One of the great gifts of ketamine is neuroplasticity of the brain. This offers temporary freedom from default-mode processing. During the medicine session, at a wildly intense level, but continued at a more subtle level for three to four days following each treatment, the mind is more flexible and expansive, with new configured synapses connections more readily available. The neuroplasticity of the mind makes it ripe for new ideas about any topic it is given to play with. Psychological defenses are lowered, and prominent, unconscious associations are more readily available. Successful work with ketamine requires that clients use this period of time to reflect on the medicine sessions and the central themes of their work.

Integration will include exploring the material of the ketamine sessions in post-medicine psychotherapy sessions, but the client will also be using the days after each treatment to talk with friends, read thoughtful material, journal, meditate, be in nature, move their body, and listen to compelling podcasts on topics related to their themes. Essentially, they should take intentional advantage of the medicine's neuroplasticity properties and give their flexible mind a lot of positive, hopeful, interesting material to respond to/engage/reconsider/dream anew.

Another strategy for using the available neuroplasticity is concrete "homework" assignments directed at increasing or decreasing particular behaviors and creating an environment for desired habit formation. Clients might have medicine sessions filled with their love of nature and respond by increasing their time in nature in the following days and weeks to build a new norm. Their session may feel meditative and awaken a wish to incorporate meditative practices into their life. They may have a psychedelic experience where they manifest a new pathway to their parent, partner, child, boss, or friend, and use the days after the session to unpack and metabolize the learnings, then try a new relational approach.

Ketamine in and of itself is unlikely to change anyone's life in a significant way. But as a fairly reliable source of epiphany and revelation, brought directly into our consulting room, it can be a bit like magic.

So, Curious?

- Worried it is way too much work to learn a whole new thing?

- Nervous about getting involved in such a new and rapidly changing part of the field?

- Daunted by the process of preparing yourself, your clients, and your practice for KAP?

I promise, if you are an established clinician who knows how to do what you do the way you do it, you can be ready to see your first KAP client within two or three months. KAP is not a developmental theory. KAP is not a practice approach. It is to be used to support your existing approach to your work with clients.

You do not need to attend a two-year advanced clinical training program to use this tool. You might want to do that sometime, as it could be rich and wonderful, but it isn't needed for experienced clinicians to start as KAP providers. Ketamine is simply a totally reasonable, realistic, practical, and massively rewarding added tool. This guidebook will walk you through each step and provide you with the necessary resources to get you started whenever you are ready.

PART ONE

ALL THE OTHER W'S

Why

Until a few years ago, I was only peripherally aware of the resurgence of psychedelic-assisted psychotherapy. While I knew psychedelics were popular among certain segments of the American population in the 1960s, I didn't register their use as particularly therapy related. In the 1980s, I remember being titillated by the prospect of MDMA use (ecstasy/molly) in clinical settings, but the discussion reeked of the Wild, Wild West, with rogue clinicians performing unsanctioned experiments that led to varying, unpredictable results. Instinctively, I appreciated the powerful possibilities this "love drug" or "truth serum" could offer if experienced in a therapist's space, but I was more interested in pursuing and developing my skills as a more classically trained psychotherapist offering outpatient psychotherapy.

For the past 30 years, I have worked as an analytically oriented psychotherapist. I have participated in ongoing professional education, as student and teacher, predominantly within my chosen frameworks of object relations/analytic/relational theory. I think there is plenty of value in other, more concrete offerings, but I have never personally felt compelled to train in any of the technique-oriented or evidence-based approaches such as cognitive behavioral therapy (CBT), dialectical behavioral therapy (DBT), or eye movement desensitization reprocessing (EMDR).

Having sat with many clients over many years, I have witnessed countless seekers find epiphany, revelation, and freedom from places they imagined they would always be stuck in. I've seen clients find resolution with parts of the self that they imagined were "just who I am." I have sat with clients a they grow/develop/evolve and build lives and relationships and professions that they found rich and rewarding. And for all the clients who make radical changes in their lives, using psychotherapy as one of their key tools, I have also seen many who are unable to free themselves. It is for this client that I was originally drawn to the tool of psychedelics.

This book isn't about me or even how I went about preparing myself, my clients, and my practice for the use of KAP. The book is, however, a response to that experience. In my journey to bring KAP into my outpatient and group practice, I found a big gap when it came to learning concrete/practical/step-by-step information. There were, and are, tons of incredible training and education opportunities in KAP and other psychedelic-assisted psychotherapies, some of which I took and loved. But one is hard pressed to find training that does not focus almost exclusively on the therapeutic contact. While of course that is the centerpiece, we also need to know how to help our clients get access to the medicine, what consent forms to use to protect our clients and ourselves, how to equip our office for medicine sessions, what forms we should use when evaluating a client for candidacy, etc. It was ridiculously complicated to gather all the relevant data and resources to move forward in a way that felt safe and solid, with all the i's dotted and t's crossed. This guide is in part my contribution to the concrete/practical/step-by-step gap in KAP literature/training/education/resources: from one clinician to another, this book covers all the basics about how to prepare yourself, your clients, and your own practice for KAP.

It is important to note here that I don't consider myself an expert in ketamine, KAP, or psychedelics, though I am a trained KAP practitioner. I am not even an expert on how to build and grow an individual or group practice, though I have successfully done both for decades. My goal here is to offer the book I couldn't find when trying to sort out all this information. This is knowledge I've gained and gathered as part of the growing community of KAP providers. I will walk you through key clinical issues, how to set up shop, work with your existing clients with this medicine, and/or add KAP-specific offerings to your clinical practice, or simply learn how to support and do integration work with clients who are working with other therapists doing psychedelic-assisted psychotherapy.

WHY I BEGAN OFFERING KAP

I was originally drawn to the field of psychotherapy because I wanted to help people, perhaps like some of you, and certainly like many of our colleagues. Truthfully, I probably wanted to save people, but I eventually understood that helping them help themselves was as close as I could get.

Given my particular clinical frame as an analytically informed psychotherapist, I often see my job as part archaeological dig supervisor and part adventure field guide. I do a lot of pointing, noticing, highlighting, and illuminating. I see my work as helping clients develop a more collaborative relationship between their conscious and unconscious selves, their intellectual understandings and their somatic experiences, and their perceptions of themselves/others/life/the world and others' perceptions of them.

For most of my clients, I offer a supportive environment, with a "beam of intense darkness," as Wilfred Bion coined, where they are encouraged to take hard looks at conflicting, nuanced truths that are compromising the lives they want to live. Doing so will help them slowly heal and repair core injuries and give them access to fuller, freer, and richer lives. For a good 20 percent of my clients, however, this is not the case.

Sometimes it becomes clear that the client's hindrance to improvement is related to me or my approach. It may be that they would do better with a different theoretical frame, perhaps a more concrete offering, a more somatic entry point into their themes, or even just a different practitioner. When this is true, I let my client know and connect them to someone with whom they can do more fruitful work.

Sometimes, though, I don't think the problem is me or my particular clinical frame. Sometimes the client's defenses, trauma, coping mechanisms, default-mode processing, fear, anxiety, deadness, and so on, are so exacerbated and entrenched that they seem unable to help themselves. Years of experience with really stuck clients is what opened me to the possibilities offered by psychedelic-assisted psychotherapies.

I overcame my reluctance to enter this less charted and still controversial part of our field because I felt unable to help some of my most precious clients. Interestingly enough, once I started working with ketamine, both exploring the medicine myself as a client and offering KAP, I came to believe that this medicine offers incredible opportunities for many more people than just my most stuck clients.

WHY I DECIDED TO WRITE THIS GUIDEBOOK

As I said earlier, I am not an expert in psychedelic-assisted psychotherapy nor in ketamine specifically. Many professionals with serious credentials and decades of experience in various fields are doing radically sophisticated research and studies that have brought us to the precipice of making multiple psychedelic medicines available for clinical use. Some of these experts have written incredible, informative, comprehensive, expansive books about this work and these medicines. Many more will be publishing in the coming years, since this field is currently exploding. They will have amazing published offerings and I will surely purchase, learn from, and promote their books.

This book, in contrast is written by a regular private-practice clinician who decided to enter the ketamine-assisted psychotherapy field a few years ago. I only recently navigated how to assess if ketamine and KAP were right for me and my practice, how and where to train, and how to onboard my private practice and group practice for this work. Because I am good at developing collaborative relationships, I connected with other clinicians who were starting their work with psychedelics, and we shared our thoughts, concerns, and frustrations about the process. Those discussions form the foundation of this book.

I am a clinician's clinician. I have always believed in our field. I believe in the diversity of our offerings, styles, education, training, theoretical approaches, and clinical techniques. I believe in the capacity of well-trained, talented, seasoned clinicians to handle complicated and difficult situations. Ketamine is a powerful medicine. As you probably know, there is much angst and caution in the world of psychedelic-assisted psychotherapy related to making sure people are properly trained to handle what happens when people take this medicine, as well there should be. Some experts suggest that people require extensive training to prepare for this work.

If the work people are attempting to prepare themselves is work as a therapist, that does indeed require extensive training. I believe it to be a wild misconception that licensed, skilled therapists need extensive additional training to enter this field. I think part of the messaging confusion is about who is being trained to do what. With so many players in the field, many training and education opportunities are trying to train too many different people to do too many different things. With little distinction between who is getting trained for what, an overview of skills is the best one could expect from many trainings.

Participants can range from:

- Licensed Psychotherapists

- Registered Nurses

- Psychology Students

- Business Professionals

- Neurologists

- Spiritual Directors

- Yoga Instructors

- Psychiatrists

Participants' end goals can range from:

- Becoming a ketamine prescriber

- Working as a ketamine-assisted psychotherapist

- Working as a second "sitter" under the supervision of a licensed provider

- Incorporating medicine sessions into therapy-adjacent retreat settings

- Providing nursing support to patients at infusion centers

The knowledge acquisition and skill development needed by each is wildly different. Even if the training/education is specifically focused on clinical contact, what a psychotherapist needs to learn to do this work well is not the same basic client contact skills someone in a non-related field needs to work as a nonclinical sitter (someone who helps support the participant through their journey, often in protocols with one clinical sitter and a secondary sitter, or in group or retreat settings), or a nurse practitioner training to become a prescriber, or a yoga instructor who is working in a retreat setting. The types of training and education each would need would vary widely.

Many programs offer one- and two-year foundational trainings. Many of these programs do not discriminate among participants' professional backgrounds. The bulk of content of these trainings is an attempt to provide basic counseling and therapeutic skills education, which does indeed take about two years. Psychotherapists have already done that education at accredited graduate education institutions. Psychotherapists are already trained for all the key components of ketamine-assisted psychotherapy, since indeed the central component is psychotherapy.

Eliminating the need for foundational skills acquisition in training signifi-cantly reduces the amount of time it takes to prepare ourselves, our clients, and our practices for KAP. This guidebook is an effort to provide the more mun-dane and practical knowledge base needed to work with ketamine and KAP.

WHY THIS BOOK IS ONLY FOR CLINICIANS

I believe there is a place for non-clinicians in the realm of healing/enlight-enment work with psychedelics. I know and have worked with some really awesome breath workers, yoga instructors, sound bath practitioners, spiritual directors, and trained sitters. They have brought powerful skills and offerings to the work as guides as well as in preparation and integration sessions, which we will cover in a bit. There will be many ways various agents of well-being and healing will begin to offer psychedelic retreats and programming in the coming years. They will have my support, with a couple of caveats.

First, psychotherapy can only be called that if it is practiced by a psycho-therapist. I think there is a place for psychedelic programs and healing that are not psychotherapy specific. But psychotherapy is indeed a specific some-thing, and its language should be reserved for psychotherapy practitioners.

Second, there are a couple parts of the clinical process of KAP during which I believe trained psychotherapists are essential. Even when the provid-ers are hoping to focus on non-therapy-type themes, like sessions focused on mindfulness, or creativity, spiritual awakening, or enlightenment, the medi-cine cannot be counted on to stay in the box we hope to place it in.

Evaluation

Outpatient psychotherapists have varying degrees of diligence regarding evaluation and assessment protocols for clients entering therapy. Some ther-apists offer a free consultation as a tool for evaluation, gather histories and/ or administer some diagnostic tools before meeting with a client; some meet with a client multiple times before really settling into a therapeutic agreement.

Among KAP practitioners, there are similarly varying protocols. Having said that, evaluation for candidacy is the starting place. While a medical prescriber will be responsible for the medical safety of the prescription, we are responsible for the clinical evaluation. Not everyone is a good match for the medicine nor the treatment. Our first job is to rule people in or out of our treatment offerings.

The clinical KAP evaluation can't be reduced to simply asking a series of questions to rule out poor candidates. Evaluating clients before proceeding with KAP requires a clinician's eye, ear, and mind. The task includes assessing the quality of the client's mind, hardly a novice skill. KAP can, in effect, "tilt reality" for clients, so we must trust that their psyche is sufficiently firm and stable enough to safely use this powerful medicine. We are evaluating the work they have done on their trauma and core anxieties, and if they have laid the right groundwork for a deep dive into their unconscious. We are assessing their expectations and will need to help them understand the limitations of the medicine and educate them about the ongoing psychotherapy work that will be required in the succeeding weeks and months. We also need to prepare them for the possibility that the medicine will not offer them the help they seek. These are clinician-level skills that require a psychotherapist to administer.

Medicine Sessions

A significant portion of each session involves a participant lying still, perhaps talking a bit, perhaps staying silent, and having a generally internal experience. It typically requires few skills to sit with participants, individually or in a group setting, as both the participant and the session are fairly self-contained.

Setting: The bulk of the work for the clinician/sitter during the medicine sessions is offering the right energetic field, emotional containment, and support for the experience: these are tasks non-clinicians can both safely offer, and excel at. In group settings, I often include sitters who are not clinicians to offer support for the client's journey, in large part, because many folx bring specific skills and capacities into the space that I cannot. I have worked with trained sitters who are also yoga instructors, breath workers, and spiritual directors, who bring their healing energy to the space to great benefit.

Trauma/Distress: Sometimes the medicine leads someone to a dark, scary, overstimulating, overwhelming, or super-activated place. When this happens, it is commonly because they connected with an internal sphere that is unfamiliar and that they generally avoid. Their unconscious and inner healing wisdom are taking them to the source of their distress/disease. In that moment, if someone is being paid to sit by their side, it should be a therapist. This is not unfamiliar territory for a seasoned psychotherapist; we know what is important to manage in these moments and what can be left to process after the fact. We will understand something of what is going on and be able to decode the symbolic expression of their themes, which will allow us to help them metabolize the truths that may surface in integration sessions down the road. We will know something of the internal terrain, and how to help a client locate safety.

Associations: The beauty of ketamine is the mental flexibility it offers. During the medicine session itself, the mind is open to unconscious connections it is usually quite defended against and disconnected from. Immediately following the medicine session, like when coming out of a dream, the mind is offering associations, which, if captured, can provide clues to the questions the participant is bringing to their work with us. Tracking and decoding unconscious associations is a well-honed skill among psychotherapists.

Ultimate Clinical Opportunity: When a participant is coming out of the ketamine psychedelic experience, the brain is still particularly fluid and flexible as a result of its capacity for neuroplasticity. This is a rich time for profound psychotherapeutic work. The work is delicate, as we are helping the client navigate new territory with no undue influence on our part, while we must also sense the places they need to lean into for deeper on-the-spot exploration. It is easy to get lost, as a client's associations can be plentiful, symbolic, and provocative. So having a therapist present during these moments after the psychedelic experience allows access to one of the great gifts of this medicine. Without a psychotherapist present, many of those gifts may go left unopened.

I suspect this book would serve as a good overview for non-clinicians interested in various elements and roles in this emerging world of psychedelic-assisted healing, which is great. But limiting the target audience for this book to licensed clinicians allowed me the delicious shorthand afforded to professional insider communication. I do not have to explain or teach or provide guidance around any of the basic counseling/therapy education that many of the big programs/books must include.

WHY THIS BOOK IS ONLY FOR *SEASONED* CLINICIANS

I am not discouraging new clinicians from entering psychedelic work. In fact, some degree programs are emerging with specific training for those who want to work clinically with psychedelics. The dilemma is this: it is a bit like trying to dance before you know how to walk. Surely you can do some creative and beautiful movements. But you won't know how to keep your balance, how to steady yourself, how to make sure you are moving forward as opposed to just moving. And if only a sloppy dance were at stake.

When we introduce psychedelics to our work, we need to feel well prepared for an unpredictable ride, with lots of moving parts, and therefore an increased need to bring all our skills to bear in the session. No one should learn how to swim in the deep end. A clinician needs to have deep familiarity with the internal terrain of the psyche. If someone is taking psychedelics just to have fun, great. If they are using them as a tool to free themselves of internal binds, they need to have a well-trained guide.

The original education that licenses clinicians to do the regular work of day-in and day-out psychotherapy is really just a spit in the bucket. We graduate with our master's or doctoral degrees, but having participated in internships and practicums, we already know the horrible truth of our field. We are entering a craft we can only get good at by doing it. The varied skills that embody our craft take years to learn. Because of this, I am suggesting that the clinician best suited to do KAP work is someone who has spent some years honing their craft, rather than someone at the very start of their career.

Who

With the field of ketamine-assisted psychotherapy rapidly expanding, we are all being regularly exposed to articles, TV shows, documentaries, and social media advertisements from online ketamine services speaking to the potentially revolutionary growth and opportunities for insight linked to this medicine. Clinicians hear from colleagues, professional bodies, friends, and family about the explosion of psychedelic-assisted psychotherapies and their use as a catalyst for important clinical work.

For clients, the possibility and promise of this medicine are real, but not for everyone or everything. For clinicians, knowing something about the way the work looks and feels and impacts the shape of our schedules are important factors for assessing if KAP is a good match for us as clinicians and for our practices. Here are some thoughts about variables that make KAP a good match for both clients and clinicians.

CLINICIANS: WHO SHOULD CONSIDER OFFERING KAP

While any licensed clinician is eligible to become a KAP provider, some might be better suited than others. Here are some of my musings on what makes a good match.

- **Realm of the Symbolic:** Again, any seasoned clinician who feels strong enough in their regular work can do KAP. It is merely an extension of our work as psychotherapists. Having said that, KAP is particularly well suited to psychotherapists with a developmental and practice frame that attends to narrative, symbolism, dreams, and associations, and/or a theoretical practice leaning toward the realm of the soma and embodiment work, and/or existential or spiritual leanings in their work. Working with clients during ketamine medicine sessions, or trips, is much like working on a dream/daydream/unconscious phantasy. Comfort and familiarity with the world of the symbolic can make this work quite rich.

- **Raw Core Material:** Having solid experience with regular psychotherapy is in my opinion a necessary qualification to work as the therapist in KAP. KAP is used in part to help clients access core material they feel defended or blocked from. We should know our way around raw experiences, trauma responses, existential quandaries, fear, grief, and epiphany. We will need our capacity for containment, reverie, floating free-association, and our skills and resilience as witnesses. In regular, ongoing work with clients, there are days when we are called to bring all of our skills to bear. One goal of introducing psychedelics into the work is to heighten clients' access to those richer, more powerful moments. We should know, and be excited by, those full, engaged, potent moments in work with clients, since we will have a greater volume and intensity of those experiences when working with psychedelics.

- **Containment Skills:** The medicine sessions require mental fluidity in the therapist, a capacity to track and make meaning out of associations, a comfort with feeling their way through a session, making use of reverie, and mining their own unconscious material for information about the client's unconscious process. The client's inner healer is offering up associations and sensations; and, especially if they are a long-term client, the value of this material will be easily visible.

- **Cognitive/Behavioral Approaches:** While medicine sessions live in a particularly narrative frame, ketamine is notably a tool for neuroplasticity, and therefore solidly in the wheelhouse of concrete behavioral and cognitive therapies as well. Ketamine reduces/derails/frees default-mode processing, allowing for the development of new neural pathways, new synapse connections, and a flexible mind. After medicine sessions, cognitive techniques and homework assignments are highly beneficial for ongoing integration work, as the neuroplasticity provided by the ketamine lasts multiple days after each session, allowing for easy access to new thoughts about old material, and the beginnings of habit formation.

- **Long- and Short-Term Work:** While KAP lends itself well to deep, symbolic, nuanced, core work, which we often imagine belonging exclusively in the purview of long-term psychotherapy, clinicians providing short-term psychotherapy are still good candidates for offering KAP if they feel comfortable and skilled at going deep. KAP is work we may be offering just to our existing psychotherapy clients, but we can also offer it as a short-term treatment option in collaboration, or occasional retreats offerings, or any number of configurations in your practice.

- **Commitment to Collaboration:** Therapists interested in KAP work should enjoy clinical team collaboration. If the client is your existing outpatient client, it is key to keep other members in the loop. As a KAP practitioner, you might work sometimes as a collateral provider, during which time it is key to collaborate with their primary therapist. This helps the KAP provider at the front end to help build a meaningful intention-setting alliance and be better prepared for what might surface and what might help. At the back end, it is the key to future integration work with their therapist.

These are simply my own musings about what a clinician might consider before entering this corner of the field, but ultimately, I think the real litmus test is how excited you feel considering it!

CLIENTS: WHO IS AND ISN'T A GOOD CANDIDATE FOR KAP?

Ketamine is a prescribed medication and will require a medical prescriber. Various medical professionals can operate as prescribers. Whatever their degrees or backgrounds, they are ultimately responsible and liable for evaluating our client for candidacy. But before sending someone to a prescriber, it serves everyone if we have done a general and clinical assessment of the fit among the client, the medicine, our treatment offerings. Let's talk first about who *isn't* a good candidate for KAP in an outpatient psychotherapy practice:

- **Thyroid/Heart/Blood Pressure:** Anyone with an untreated and insufficiently treated thyroid, heart, or blood pressure condition. I ask this medical question on my intake evaluation, not so I can rule anyone in or out, since I only practice within my non-medical scope, but so that I can alert or consult with the prescriber before their medical evaluation. The prescribing medical professional may support the client's use of ketamine given their specific condition and medications. I am still at liberty to recommend that, given their medical compromise, they get their ketamine treatment at an infusion center, where medical monitoring and intervention is available, for their safety/protection/comfort or mine.

- **Schizophrenia or Schizoaffective Disorder:** Anyone with a diagnosis or history of schizophrenia or schizoaffective disorder. A highly skilled, highly knowledgeable clinician with extensive experience with both ketamine and schizophrenia might feel comfortable with their capacity to assess risk and then feel comfortable treating that client with ketamine. But my motto is better safe than sorry for both me and the client. I would direct this client to work with the other psychedelic medicines as they become available, as they are not similarly contraindicated, or refer them to someone with particular expertise.

- **Reality-Testing Capacity:** Clients who have difficulty with reality testing, paranoia, magical thinking, maintaining a clear train of thought, or other forms of "loose" thinking. This is based on our clinical assessment and unless our prescriber is clinically educated, the burden of this assessment is on us. During the ketamine sessions, clients are invited into a very surreal world where thoughts take shape and magical enactments play out. Upon rousing from their ketamine medicine session experience, it is important that they have a capacity/inclination toward cognitive clarity.

- **Bipolar and Mania:** Anyone with a diagnosis or history of bipolar disorder or episodes of mania. Ketamine can trigger a manic episode in anyone with a predisposition. I am aware of and supportive of some clinicians who, with some clients, determine together that it is worth the risk. I do not offer KAP to clients with any history of mania. Neither MDMA (ecstasy) nor psilocybin (mushrooms) are contraindicated for mania. I encourage those clients to consider getting involved with one of the current FDA psychedelic trials for MDMA or psilocybin, or wait until one of those two becomes available legally for psychedelic-assisted psychotherapy.

- **Clients in Recovery from Substance Use Disorders:** I have worked with people who have chosen to abstain from mind-altering substances for years and then decide to break their no-drug stance to engage in KAP. I have done KAP with clients otherwise in recovery, but usually only with my own clients whom I have worked with for a very long time, or in very active collaboration with their ongoing therapist. While psilocybin and ketamine have been studied as a treatment for people with active substance use disorders, the risk level is much different for a person in multi-year recovery who decides to take a mood and mind-altering substance. While lots of KAP clinicians have anecdotal data that implies that risks are low for clients to relapse after ketamine treatments, it is still imperative that client and clinician have a solid plan in place in case it happens.

Okay, now who *is* a good candidate in an outpatient private practice?

- **Seasoned Travelers:** The ideal client has long since started their exploration into themselves. They know their inner landscape and are able to think and talk about it. KAP is not the place to start a deep dive. It is a tool to help people who have already been doing their inner work, are familiar with their themes, and have developed concepts and language to talk about their internal world. It is a gateway to our most stuck and defended places: clients benefit from intimate knowledge of the territory.

- **The Very Stuck Client:** What ketamine offers in the medicine session itself, but also in the days that follow, is access to a flexible, expansive mind that is capable of generating new thoughts around old themes. The client who feels particularly stuck or who can't imagine a new narrative is a great candidate for KAP. This includes people with obsessive compulsive disorders, body dysmorphia, post-traumatic stress disorders, eating disorders, or other conditions that limit mental creativity and imagination. It is useful for people stuck in depression, anxiety, or grief who can't conceptualize a different approach to life. It can offer a wildly new narrative for those seeking a resolution of a trauma or conflict. At its essence, it can help create movement where there was little.

- **Clients with Treatment-Resistant Depression:** Two-thirds of people with treatment-resistant depression who have never benefited significantly from other antidepressants experience a reduction in symptoms of depression from ketamine itself. Unlike other antidepressants, ketamine impacts the glutamate system. When taken with a certain protocol, commonly once or twice a week for four to eight weeks, with booster doses every month to few months, it can help alleviate symptoms of depression. KAP practices work with a large number of clients with treatment-resistant depression.

- **Seekers:** Some clients come to ketamine and KAP for purposes of enlightenment, epiphany, and spiritual growth, which are lovely and relevant uses of the medicine. (To qualify for a prescription, clients will need to be able to report symptoms of depression or anxiety.) This likely means fewer KAP sessions as they are not necessarily trying to work through a specific theme. This is work that can often happen in retreat and group settings. Like with all KAP work, integration remains key.

- **Those with Very Empty Wells:** For some of my clients who suffer the most, at least part of the dilemma is they simply haven't benefited from enough basic experiences of goodness/love/safety/joy in their lives. They haven't really gotten enough of a fill. When I was 20 years old in college, I watched *Mister Rogers' Neighborhood* almost every day after classes for a year. I knew I had never been exposed to the self-loving messages that show was pouring on children across the nation. I spent a year watching, listening, and using it to fill myself up a bit. Ketamine sessions can be magical.

They can be some of life's peak experiences. One reason to engage in KAP is to try to connect with goodness and love and beauty to store inside the self.

- **Some of Your Existing Clients:** KAP is best done in the context of an existing therapeutic relationship, as an extension of ongoing work. The existing relationship provides deep familiarity with the work the client is doing, the backstories, relevant players, associations, and stuck places, which can all enrich the KAP work. It is particularly rewarding as a clinician when you can offer KAP to your own client. It is worth thinking about each of your clients and who might benefit from the treatment option. As you familiarize yourself with the tool over time, you will notice in sessions who and what and when KAP might help.

- **You:** You are likely a great candidate for KAP. You are surely a seasoned traveler, likely a serious seeker, and given that you are human, must have some stuck themes you work on routinely. One way to understand what ketamine and KAP can offer your client is to explore the medicine yourself. If you have qualifying symptoms of anxiety or depression to acquire a prescription, doing a round of KAP yourself will help you see ways various clients might also make use of this treatment.

Where

As seasoned clinicians, most of us have well-established professional networks. We know where to get our practices' needs met. We know our annual licensing education requirements and how we like to fulfill them. We have clinical networks for referrals and collaboration that include medical and psychiatric providers. We know how to access resources we or our clients may need within the larger clinical community.

Adding KAP to our toolset requires some adjustments and additions to our networks. While it is a bit daunting to add a tool to our practices that so few of our fellow clinicians know much about, there are only a handful of things we need to get started.

WHERE TO TRAIN FOR PSYCHEDELIC-ASSISTED PSYCHOTHERAPY

Throughout this guide, I present occasional elements that go against the grain of opinion of a portion of the psychedelic-assisted psychotherapy movement. Wherever that is true, I will highlight them, offer their argument, and explain mine. I suspect my stance regarding the amount of training a seasoned clinician needs in order to add this tool to their work is among my controversial opinions.

Here is what I noticed as I pursued education in KAP: A lot of people in my classes/groups/workshops were not psychotherapists, nor were the bulk of the trainers. While the participants hoped to be involved in psychedelic-assisted psychotherapy, many did not have the clinical education or professional experience of sitting with clients day in and day out, week after week, year after year, which to me is an obvious prerequisite to doing anything with the word "psychotherapy" in it.

Participants in a large percentage of KAP training/education offerings include medical professionals and scientists, psychotherapists, meditation and yoga educators, spiritual directors, breath and sound guides, life coaches, counselors and people who have studied psychology/mental health, business folx considering a change in career, people working in hospital settings, and some folx simply interested in psychedelics. It can make the education fascinating, but poses a educational dilemma; if participants in a training about the provision of ketamine-assisted psychotherapy aren't psychotherapists, they need to be taught some psychotherapy 101.

For me, this is problematic for two reasons:

- As one of the psychotherapists in the room, I have no interest in psychotherapy 101. If I am going to talk about transference and countertransference in a ketamine session, I want to do it with folx who have years of knowledge about what that feels like in clinical work, not with people conceptualizing it for the first time, often with a trainer who isn't even a psychotherapist by trade.

- For participants in a training who are not psychotherapists, and understand they won't be providing the psychotherapy component of KAP, 101 can be great as an overview. For medical folx administering infusions, trained sitters in a group setting, prescribers not particularly familiar with psychotherapy, an overview of psychotherapy basics would help them understand aspects of what they might encounter in their particular roles. But a two-year program is a clinical training program. Delicious. If you are already licensed to work as a psychotherapist. If you aren't a therapist, one of two things is true:

» You either don't need this in-depth training, since you won't be able to work as a psychotherapist, KAP or otherwise, without attending an accredited institution for a master's-level degree in a psychotherapy field.

» You want to become trained as a psychotherapist. Great. Go do that. At an accredited institution for a master's-level degree in a psychotherapy field.

So while I do not think licensed clinicians need skills training in how to sit with a client, nor theoretical education on how to unpack dreams with a client, I do believe some KAP overview training is in order. There are many well-reputed programs. I am not in a position to provide recommendations beyond this:

- **Clinician-Specific Education:** Attend a program specifically for clinicians.

- **Ketamine-Specific Education:** If you hope to offer KAP, you need some focus on ketamine itself, as opposed to other psychedelics, as ketamine's properties, uses, and administrations are unique.

- **Live, Synchronous Learning:** Opportunities to ask questions, engage in discussion, and begin building a sense of community are hugely important, so synchronous is best.

- **Networking Opportunities:** Successful entry in KAP work requires networking and collaboration. Attend a program that facilitates that so you can start to build the village in which you will do this work. If you can train locally, even better.

- **Starter Kit Training:** My personal recommendation is that a short overview program is the best way for licensed clinicians to get started. For me, as is true for many psychotherapists, learning is a lifelong endeavor, to which we devote ongoing time and effort. Personally, I have and will continue to learn about KAP, as I continue to study my other work loves, like object relations theory, for the rest of my career/life. The issue at hand is what you need to know to get started. Every therapist started their careers with the terrifying truth; the only way to learn our trade is by sitting with the client. Unfortunately, that is true about KAP as well; you will have to figure it out along the way. No amount of training is going to eliminate the need to learn on the job. Be brave. If you are a seasoned clinician, it won't be your first time being terribly brave.

- **Seek Out Practicum/Internship/Mentorship/Supervision Opportunities:** I have watched many licensed clinicians interested in KAP work become convinced they need years of education and training to become sufficiently prepared. I strongly disagree and believe what most practicing psychotherapists need is much more mundane and practical. One of my efforts to support onboarding new practitioners is this guidebook. The other effort is a short, practicum-focused program for licensed clinicians—a joint project I offer along with my most trusted KAP colleague, through the education wing of each of our group practices, Ketamine Kollaborations. It includes basic educational components specific to working with ketamine and KAP; but the key component is a supervised KAP practicum experience with each therapist's own client. We can't read or study ourselves into mastery. We have to just jump in and start doing the work. My last recommendation is to find a practicum or mentorship program, a KAP supervisor, or meeting with a collection of KAP providers. We learn by doing, but hopefully in a supported way.

WHERE DO CLIENTS GET PRESCRIPTIONS?

Despite ketamine's legal status for off-label use to treat depression and anxiety, the vast majority of medical professionals are not comfortable or interested in prescribing the medicine. They are understandably concerned about the implications of prescribing a medicine for off-label use, with high risk for misuse, that is perceived with stigma and mistrust by the general population, and that certainly would require an increase in their malpractice insurance policy. These factors can make it difficult for our clients to access the medicine in an affordable way. Here are some avenues to explore when setting up shop:

The Client's Psychiatrist

If the client has an existing psychiatrist or prescriber of psychotropic medicines, that person is an important place to start. While it is highly unlikely that the average psychiatrist is going to be open to prescribing ketamine for their client, when it works, it is the best model for everyone involved. Even if it doesn't result in the psychiatrist prescribing the client ketamine, collaboration is an essential component of our work with all our clients, and with ketamine, it is appropriate that at a minimum the psychiatrist be kept in the loop.

Because most medical professionals are reluctant to get involved with the move toward psychedelic interventions, many KAP providers are bypassing them completely. I understand the impulse. Devoting time engaging with medical professionals who are often staunchly opposed to and dismissive of the possibilities in these medicines and ignorant of KAP as a treatment model is the least pleasant, or even productive, part of my week. But, in my opinion, bypassing them constitutes extreme professional disrespect.

One of the services I offer clients who are interested in KAP is a free initial consultation with their psychiatrist. After the client has initiated a conversation with their prescriber and authorized an exchange of information, I send the prescriber multiple articles and resources about ketamine and KAP and make myself available for a conversation.

I do this for four reasons. First, it is basic professional courtesy/ethical practice to involve them in this important decision, even if reluctant, opposed, or dismissive. Second, we might succeed, and that is the most convenient and well-integrated option for the client. Third, they may end up being a resource for our work as a KAP referral source or even agree to prescribe for our other KAP clients. Fourth, exposure to these conversations with clinicians involved in KAP is a public education initiative.

Building a Collaborative Relationship with a Local Prescriber

You might successfully find a couple of psychiatrists or other prescribers in your network who are open to prescribing ketamine. If so, it is worth investing time building a collaborative relationship. Different prescribers might vary in their approaches or have certain circumstances they will or will not support, for instance, dosage amounts, number of doses, or whether they will support at-home use or only in-office use during KAP sessions. It is worth cultivating options for your clients. Establishing a couple of solid relationships with prescribers who can collaboratively engage around issues like dosing and frequency protocols is worth the effort.

Online National Prescribers

There are multiple online national prescribers who offer tele-health medical consultations with clients and send ketamine prescriptions directly to the client's home for at-home use. These are some of the easiest, most convenient ways to access the medicine. Some of the online programs can be quite pricey, depending on the additional services, but some can be the cheapest, most convenient option out there, making them highly appealing.

There is much legitimate controversy, concern, and criticism in the field of KAP about the online, multi-state tele-health providers. Some of the concern centers on how little oversight or monitoring of the client is possible with a large organizational tele-health model. There are concerns regarding dosing, frequency, extended periods of treatment, risk of abuse, misuse, and addiction in the absence of a live, local relationship with a prescribert. Most have a complete absence of collaboration with the client's other providers, including possible KAP providers, and some have no requirements at all that the patient be involved in psychotherapy or KAP. There is criticism that some services appear therapy-like but are not actually therapy, and others are criticized for offering no KAP-type services or therapy expectations at all.

While I support all these concerns, prior to finding and developing strong relationships with local prescribers, I often relied on these online services for my own clients. It is currently still very difficult to find consistent, reliable, timely access to ketamine prescribers outside of these online programs. So, while I share some of these concerns, I believe these companies are successfully providing access to this important medicine.

WHERE DO WE WORK WITH OUR CLIENTS?

A key part of the clinical frame for KAP is the setting, at least in part a reference to the physical setting of the medicine session. The settings in which we offer KAP can vary widely.

What each medicine session setting shares in common is that the KAP journey does not begin with the medicine session. Before a client lands in the physical location where they will be using ketamine to enter a medicine journey, they will have had multiple prior contacts with the KAP provider. They will have been clinically evaluated, supported to meet with a prescriber, and done at least one, if not multiple, preparation sessions. Preparation sessions will have prepared them both practically and psychologically for the medicine session. These sessions also serve to ready the therapist for material that may come up in their session.

Similarly, regardless of where the medicine session takes place, it isn't the last phase of their journey. Integration efforts, in the minutes/hours/days/weeks following the session will be key to client's leveraging their experience to change their lives. The bulk of relevant work in KAP will happen in the therapist's consultation space, regardless of the location of the medicine session, because ultimately, KAP is just psychotherapy.

Infusion Centers

Embedded in the functions of infusion centers are inherent disruptions to the experience of a medicine journey, making it the least ideal environment. Despite this, some clients will do some or all their medicine sessions at these centers. Sometimes indicated due to physical conditions requiring medical oversight, co-existing conditions like pain or migraines that may be concurrently treated with ketamine, seeking particular treatment-resistant depression protocols, or having insurance that covers treatment only by infusion, these centers are the site of many a medicine experience.

Besides the less-than-ideal environment, for the most part, ketamine infusion centers are not providing or offering facilitated access to ketamine-assisted psychotherapy to their patients. The infusion center is relying solely on ketamine itself as a molecule to aid in symptom reduction. Like many treatments they offer patients, the infusion itself is treated simply as the administration of a medication. Most centers are not particularly aware of the psychedelic experience beyond its interest as a novelty, nor are they knowledgable about the medicine's boosting effect on the brain's neuroplasticity. Few centers are supporting their patients in making meaningful use of the medicine session experience, nor the client's flexible mind.

Usually when our client is having their medicine sessions at infusion centers, we are unable to actually sit with them during the infusion. The KAP work we do with them will be the original evaluation and on-boarding, preparation before the start of their work with ketamine, preparation and integration therapy sessions interspersed between their medicine treatment sessions, and ways we support their between-session activities.

Occasionally, we might collaborate with an infusion center that allows us to come in and sit with our clients while the medical staff handle the infusion and monitoring. When providing KAP services in an infusion center, we need to offer as many comforts as possible, for example:

- Secure a private room when possible.

- Suggest the client wear comfortable clothes.

- Suggest the client bring a nice blanket and eye shades.

- If the client is going to use a soundtrack, they should have headphones. You two should negotiate a volume that helps them reduce the distractions of the environment but still allows them to talk with you when desired.

- Dim the lights if possible.

- Set up your chair near the client but out of the way of the medical staff.

- Make sure your client knows that monitors will beep a lot, the blood pressure cuff will squeeze their arm every 15 minutes, they may hear chatter; emphasize that their job is to go internal.

- The medical staff will need a few minutes to set up various monitoring systems and prepare the infusion. Once the actual infusion begins, the client will move very quickly into an altered state. If the infusion center staff are cooperative, ask them to give you a few minutes after they get everything all set up but before they begin the infusion. Use this to help the client prepare for their journey: touch base and connect around their intention, take some deep breaths, maybe read a meditation or poem, and get into a good space for beginning their session.

- Depending on the level/capacity of cooperation with the medical staff, see if you two can stay in the room after the medicine infusion, for some clinical time. These 20 minutes after the session are precious in terms of neuroplasticity, lowered defenses, and access to the details of the psychedelic experience. While the client may still be a bit groggy, they are ripe with relevant loose associations you can collect for processing in your follow-up integration sessions.

Outpatient Practice Settings

The bulk of KAP sessions across the country take place in outpatient settings with therapists in the same outpatient offices the use to do the rest of their psychotherapy session. We originally set up our spaces to provide psychotherapy, with elements that facilitated our clients' comfort. KAP simply requires a handful of additional considerations.

- Long-enough couch or portable bed for lying down, with pillows and blankets. You might consider an optional weighted blanket because some people like the feeling of weight on them during a session.

- A small cup for them to place their medicine in when they arrive. You should not be touching/dispensing their medication for liability reasons.

- Eye shades, which you can provide or have the client bring. If you are going to purchase them, I recommend form-fitting, 3D eye shades.

- If clients are going to use a soundtrack, they should have headphones or a volume that can work for you both. You two should negotiate a volume that helps them reduce the distractions of the environment but still allows them to talk with you when desired.

- In case the client feels nauseous, it is good to have disposable sick bags and a cloth for them to use in case they get sick.

- If clients will be using a protocol where they spit the medicine out after swirling it in their mouths, you will need a cup for them to spit into.

- Some clinicians like to provide a very small cup of juice, hard candy, or Tic Tac, in case the client has difficulty with the taste after spitting or swallowing the medicine.

- Access to a bathroom on the same floor as the office. You will invite the client to use the restroom right before ingesting the medicine, but if they need to use it again during their medicine session, they will be unsteady on their feet. You will assist them, but stairs aren't reasonable.

- An assortment of snacks/food/beverages for after their journey, since they may have fasted.

- A planned ride home from the medicine session.

Group Retreat Settings

Retreats are a great environment for offering KAP. While some elements of preparation will have to happen before the retreat, and some aspects of integration happen after the retreat, it is a great way to offer a holistic, comprehensive experience. The medicine itself is not particularly communal in nature, as per the medicine sessions themselves. But the acts and rituals of preparation and integration are great for community building. And the chance to be in community when accessing these short, powerful experiences takes full advantage of the opportunities the medicine offers.

The term "retreat" usually refers to a weekend or longer getaway, where participants sleep over and engage in lots of programming and group experiences. The same is true for KAP retreats, which usually include two or more medicine sessions and lots of offerings to prepare for the sessions and integrate them. Certainly, talk therapy-type activities are common, but so are rituals, meditation, art and journaling exercises, sound baths, walks in nature, and the like, all to facilitate a good mindset, a communal experience, and a well-focused intention.

The environment would need the same items and setup as listed above for the outpatient practice setting, with the addition of mats/pillow/blankets for all of your participants, sitting mats for the therapists, a circle seating area, some art or journal writing supplies, and perhaps an "altar" of sorts to facilitate a group process.

At-Home Ketamine Use

Most of the national online prescribing companies are prescribing for at-home ketamine use. The bulk of their customers are not involved with any accompanying psychotherapy. Many programs offer an array of materials and services to support a therapeutic experience, with intention-setting prompts, guides available through text, maybe even a video conference right before and immediately following the first medicine session, on-boarding audio and music for medicine sessions, and sometimes guide-led integration circles with other participants. The quality and quantity vary from company to company, but there are some solid, if costly, offerings.

These companies hold all the liability related to prescribing for at-home use. Personally, I have used and I support these companies. They are making this very important medicine available to clients who otherwise may be unable to get a prescription. Before identifying local prescribers, I often directed clients to these options if their own psychiatrist was unwilling to prescribe or unwilling to prescribe for at-home use. For our clients, who are indeed involved in KAP, the therapy-like material supports and services offered by the prescribing companies are lovely supplemental materials for their journeys.

To make KAP an affordable option for a wider range of clients, most of my clients do the bulk of their medicine sessions at home. That is not the case with many of my colleagues, but that is one of the options. Here are three sample models:

- Clients can take the medicine at home, on their own, with another adult at the residence, while still doing active KAP work with us.

  » Initial Sessions: Typically, I facilitate one to three live medicine sessions with the client in my office when they are first beginning

KAP treatment, both to find the right dose and to familiarize them with the medicine. If they are familiar with non-ordinary states, and/or have tried psychedelics before, they may feel comfortable doing the sessions on their own from the beginning.

» Support for Their Support Person: We can offer guidance and direction for an at-home adult during their medicine session. This might be in the form of a preparation session or check-in, with them and the adult, to go over material they may find helpful and to answer their questions. I also include in their preparation packet a write-up for their support person. I sometimes offer to be in a text exchange with them and their support person during the hours of the planned medicine session.

» Preparation and Integration Sessions: Our work will be focused on preparation and integration sessions. We will not be present for the actual medicine session but will help the client build intention before each session, process the experience in subsequent sessions, and work toward integration of the material and experience.

» Sometimes, if clients want to use a twice-a-week protocol, I might offer half sessions virtually, so that we can have two or three short sessions a week to help them make sense of each session and prepare for the next.

» While using the at-home model, we might still do an occasional medicine session together for clinical reasons related to their material or in case of difficulty making good use of the medicine session.

» I strongly support this model primarily because it is the most financially feasible for most clients. As a social worker, I seek to make this medicine accessible to a larger population. Some clients are not well suited for at-home use, but if finances are a consideration, I am not quick to rule it out.

- Clients can take the medicine at home, while we sit with them over telehealth.

  » Never in a million years would I have ever thought that any relevant psychotherapy could/would/should happen over video. And then the pandemic happened. While I still do not consider video ideal, despite its popularity among clients due to its convenience, it is most certainly a legitimate way to do our work.

  » While clients might find it a bit odd to have us watching them lie down with eye shades in their own homes, we can make that comfortable fairly easily.

  » This allows us to do a medicine session but not have to deal with the issues associated with their getting safely back home.

  » If a client is going to be taking a lower psychelytic dose, this means we can still use the session for a talk exploration.

  » They would still need that other adult in the residence who is prepared to support them in order to meet the liability needs of most prescribers.

- Another hybrid option is for clients to take the medicine at home, and we do virtual prep or integration sessions right before they administer the medicine and as they are rousing from the medicine session.

  » For clients taking a psychedelic dose of the medicine, most do very little talking. In fact, when they do, we are often directing them to talk less and go internal. Given this, for financial reasons, it is reasonable for some clients to not want to pay for us to sit with them during the medicine session itself.

» Having a session, or even half a session, right before clients take the medicine, can help them to secure their intention in mind and cultivate a generative mindset. We might even use some of that time to help them with a short breathing or meditative exercise, read them a poem, or listen to music together.

» Once clients are familiar with the length of their medicine sessions, we can schedule an unpacking/integration session immediately following the medicine session. This is a time of great mental flexibility, with loose associations, lowered defenses, and a chance to capture by talking something of their experience while it is still just a cloud wisp away.

Obviously, we can do a combination of all of the above. Like the medicine's effects, our treatment structure is best managed with some fluidity, flexibility, and adaptability to the specific needs of our clients and different outposts in their journey.

When

While becoming a KAP psychotherapist doesn't require learning a new developmental theory or clinical treatment theory, the details can feel a bit overwhelming.

WHEN DO WE DO WHAT?

In the first six-week practicum/training cycle I co-facilitated through Ketamine Kollaborations, one of the therapists, in a moment of overwhelm, asked, "But when do you do what? Like, specifically?" This section is a response to that question.

Obviously, there are many ways to approach the flow of events, but here are a few models.

Steps for Clients Reaching Out Specifically for KAP

If you have decided to advertise as a KAP practitioner, and someone is reaching out specifically for KAP services, here is a sample flow of events:

- Send initial interest email that includes:
  - » Outline of your process/steps

» Articles/information about KAP/ketamine to begin educating the client about the treatment

» Intake form to assess client candidacy

- Review Intake Form

  » Rule Out: If your intake form indicates they are a poor candidate because of clear medical or psychological contraindications, inform them they are not a good candidate, either for ketamine in general or perhaps simply not for your practice. If the contraindications are medical and you have a prescriber you can discuss the case with, you might later decide to proceed. Depending on the situation, you might refer them to other psychedelic practitioners, practices, or infusion centers better suited to work with them. Rule In: If the intake form does not eliminate the candidate, schedule an initial consultation to continue the evaluation process. While brief, here are some features of this first consultation:

    – I typically do this for free, even though it takes 20 to 30 minutes, because I am still evaluating the client for candidacy, and as a public education service.

    – Review anything of note from the intake form, like a history of trauma, experience with non-ordinary states, status of conversations with their psychotherapist and/or psychiatrist, etc.

    – Access the quality of their mind. If we see difficulty with reality testing, particularly disorganized thinking capacity, or signs of an unstable mental capacity, we might rule the client out, or lengthen the period of evaluation over multiple sessions.

- Discuss their hopes and expectations for the session. Start to build the concept of intention. Start to manage expectations.

- Further assess if they are a good match for the medicine and for your specific offerings/practice. I offer both individual and group KAP sessions, so I will be helping us assess which is better suited to their needs/situation.

- Begin educating and informing on how the medicine works, how KAP works, how my particular services work, what it will cost, and their next steps.

- Review plans for connecting with a prescriber as well as plans for any collaboration meetings with their therapist and/or psychiatrist when appropriate.

- Follow-up email:

  » Next Steps: Outline next steps with a prescriber and any plans for collaboration meetings with their therapist and/or psychiatrist when appropriate.

  » Supplemental Materials: Include reading material about ketamine, KAP, and more specifically about intention setting and material you hope they use to formulate a vision for their work.

- Professional Collaboration: If you make contact with their psychiatrist and/or therapist, email them with a similar outline of the process, attaching some articles as resources. They may have interest in consulting with you about this particular shared client and/or KAP in general.

- Start KAP treatment: Once the client is ready to move forward, start scheduling preparation sessions. You can do this before they secure their medication.

» Preparation sessions cover administrative elements like consent forms, education about the medicine and process, as well as the clinical work of curating the right mindset and developing intentions for upcoming medicine sessions.

» Number of Preparation Sessions: Most practitioners recommend a minimum of two or three preparation sessions before the medicine session. The number is impacted by variables related to familiarity with the client, trauma history, indications for prolonged assessment, etc.

    – Clients will have many questions, especially if they struggle with anxiety. There is no need to rush to the medicine session. Their questions hold important clues to issues they might well address with this medicine.

    – Group Q&A: My shortcut for some of the more mundane aspects of preparation is a virtual group Q&A. If I have multiple clients interested in on-boarding with KAP in a similar time frame, or for a group retreat, I handle the general parts of preparation this way. It reduces cost for the client, reduces isolation around proceeding with a novel treatment, and, in the case of group retreats, begins building a sense of community for the participants.

» Build Shared Language: Cover the three ways the medicine can be helpful: as a molecule with a certain protocol, the psychedelic experience, and the resulting neuroplasticity. Preparation sessions will explore ways to leverage these three facets of KAP in terms of decisions regarding protocols for frequency, dosing, structure of sessions, and activities between sessions. Building shared language and concepts will aid in these many conversations.

» Plan Dosing Protocols: Discuss if you plan to use psychelytic or psychedelic doses, and how you will explore dosing in the first sessions. While your prescriber dictates the parameters of the client's dosing, we may choose to have the client start at lower doses for various reasons.

» Safety Planning: Explore history of trauma, existential questions, and other concerns about material that might show up as difficult experiences. Build plans for how you two will manage difficult elements of the medicine session.

» Consents: Consents are not just forms to be signed; they are concepts to be explored. This includes general consents to engage in KAP, touch, or at-home consents.

  – If you intend to make physical touch available during the medicine session, like hand holding, preparation sessions are where you discuss the parameters, provide touch-refusal exercises, and come to shared agreements.

  – Review all consent elements prior to the live session and have them signed either before the day of the medicine session or on the day of the medicine session, before they self-administer their medicine.

» Music Plan: If you intend to use music during the medicine session, you and your client will need to collaborate on shared goals for the session and decide who will supply the playlist.

» Post-Medicine Session Plan: Prior to their first medicine journey, they need an established plan for post-medicine session transportation, and/or a sufficiently prepared support person for their at-home session.

» Prior to the First Medicine Session: Email the client a guide to the week/days/hours before and after the medicine sessions, and a write-up about/for the adult(s) in their lives who are going to be supporting them immediately after the session. If the client will be taking their medicine at home, send an outline reminder of the expectations of the adult who will be sitting with them.

Preparation can take as long as you and your client find beneficial. There are no set protocols that limit preparation. Some clients have sufficient eagerness to move the process along. Some reveal an amount of ambivalence that suggests slowing down and regrouping. Some have angst or nervousness that may require our support to sufficiently manage before proceeding.

Once the medicine sessions have begun, the rhythm and pacing, while discussed in your initial preparation session, will still ultimately be up to you and your client to continually assess as you go along.

Steps for Our Ongoing Clients Who Want to Try KAP

For existing clients in your outpatient therapy practice, the same steps can be easily woven in over a longer timeline. Preparation activities can be sprinkled over months of therapy, dipping in and out while doing the regular work of therapy. Medicine sessions themselves may happen only occasionally, and integration work becomes just another word for therapy.

I've had clients I was particularly eager to have try KAP. I have been surprised when some haven't shared my enthusiasm for something so potentially game changing. In other cases, I have clients who jump so high at the chance to do KAP, I worry they are idealizing the treatment. The anxieties, urgencies, ambivalence, hopes, concerns, lethargy, excitement, preoccupation, reluctance, etc., are all grist for the mill and provide opportunities for in-depth, unhurried exploration.

PART TWO

AND NOW FOR THE HOW: TOOLING FOR KAP

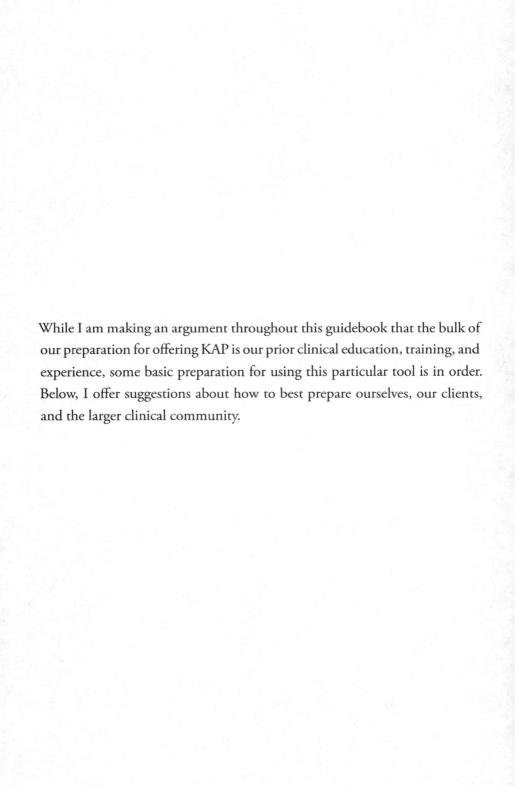

While I am making an argument throughout this guidebook that the bulk of our preparation for offering KAP is our prior clinical education, training, and experience, some basic preparation for using this particular tool is in order. Below, I offer suggestions about how to best prepare ourselves, our clients, and the larger clinical community.

Preparing Yourself

The best preparation to do this work is having a solid psychotherapy education and some years of experience in clinical practice. Here are some other variables that will help you feel prepared to do this work safely:

EDUCATION/TRAINING

A plethora of psychedelic trainings are available these days, locally and nationally, at week-long conferences and via virtual, asynchronous courses. There are a range of target audiences, from prescribers to psychotherapists to people interested in trying the medicines. The topics range from the science of ketamine, how to best make use of the trip, curating a good musical playlist, or how to support legalization of all the medicines. While I do not feel knowledgeable enough to provide program-specific recommendations, I do have some general recommendations in the prior section "Where to We Train."

It is easy when surveying the education opportunities to get lulled into the idea that you are underprepared for this work without extensive, additional training. It is also easy just to get lured by the awesomeness of the offerings. We can take as many trainings and workshops as we desire. But that doesn't mean we need them in order to get started.

For experienced clinicians, we will learn about how to incorporate this tool into our work by doing KAP work with our clients. Rather than skill training, we need practical, concrete information about the medicine, protocols, steps, contraindications, consent forms, acquiring prescriptions for our clients, evaluating risks, etc. Whatever programs you consider, make sure they intend to directly help you implement offering this treatment to your clients.

CREDENTIALING

Ideally, there would be an established credentialing body to provide clear guidelines about education/training/supervision requirements for KAP. Unfortunately, psychedelic-assisted psychotherapy is currently being offered without a designated governing body or clear guidelines. Credentialing bodies are in the works, with competing stakeholders, negotiating all the who's/how's/what's. Complicating the process is that, unlike a credentialing body for one specific profession, these bodies are attempting to determine what qualifies individuals in many professions—from anesthesiologists and nurse practitioners, to psychiatrists and social workers, to yoga instructors and trained sitters. There are additionally multiple medicines and multiple proposed settings. All of these factors need to get teased out.

A very active national listserv, *Big Tent*, exists for licensed professionals in the psychedelic world. The participants include medical prescribers and assisted psychotherapy providers. Besides random practitioners like me, the listserv is populated by the leaders in the field. As I read the passionate debates around dosing, frequency, at-home use, unlicensed sitters, two-clinician versus one-clinician protocols, it is clear that coming to agreements about who/how/what is going to be no easy task.

For licensed clinicians, however, our own licensing bodies allow us to do our work. What we are offering is psychotherapy. We are not prescribers. We are not providing or administering medication to our clients. I have had clients take Klonopin or Ativan during sessions and I don't carry extra liability as a result. Ketamine is not an illegal substance. It is a prescribed medication.

In the current absence of an official credentialing body, it would be important to access training through well-established programs and maintain documentation of everything you have done, so that when the time comes, you will likely have met the bulk of the requirements for certification. This includes tracking hours of offering service and any supervision from other KAP-trained clinicians.

MALPRACTICE INSURANCE

Increasingly, malpractice insurance companies are offering coverage of sorts for KAP. The language is vague and has not been trial-tested against any lawsuit claims. Always important to remember, though: we are not the prescribers.

The language used by companies that offer specific liability waivers for KAP indicates that we are covered as long as our work is "in our scope of practice." At a concrete, practical level, this means we do not prescribe, store, handle, administer the medicine, or provide any medical services to clients.

It is prudent to work with a company willing to put something in writing specifically mentioning KAP. It can take quite a few phone calls, but the more of us making those calls to our various insurance providers, the more standard this coverage will become.

TRYING THE MEDICINE OURSELVES

One of the first questions clinicians considering providing KAP face is if we intend to try the medicine ourselves as a means of increasing our understanding of its use as a tool. While a reasonable reason to try the medicine, just as legitimate a reason is the opportunities for healing it will offer us. This is a unique tool, which can be leveraged to further our journey toward actualization. Our knowledge of our inner workings makes us particularly exciting candidates for the opportunities of KAP. The more skills a participant has to work with their unconscious mind, to read their somatic experience, to know something about the direction they want to lead their journey, the more potent the possibilities are in a medicine session. Psychotherapists who try this medicine are likely to have beautifully important sessions they can use to further their own healing.

And then, yes, it is additionally true that using the medicine ourselves can indeed significantly help us support our KAP clients. As a rule, I do not subscribe to a view that shared experiences inherently improve our ability to join with our clients, explore empathetic and sympathetic responses, projectively identify with, or reliably witness their experience. That said, for many clinicians, this is a reasonable opportunity to have way more information about a treatment tool. Clients will have seemingly endless questions about the many details related to KAP treatment, and your own experience will support your confidence in answering.

Like all people interested in trying the medicine, we must be able to report symptoms of depression or anxiety in order to acquire a prescription. If we are able to meet this criterion, we can access the medicine in the same manner as our clients. There may be a time when this medicine is available for spiritual and enlightenment purposes, but for now, it is part of a medical model, which therefore requires a diagnosis.

I am aware I repeatedly use the word "tool" to describe this medicine. That is definitely my central concept for its use. In my own experience of taking the medicine, I needed to take it many times to learn how to use it as a finely tuned instrument. Just as our experiences as clients inform our practices, much can be learned about how this medicine works through experience.

If you are interested in exploring the medicine, consider a KAP-trained therapist or KAP retreat. Alternatively, if you are in a KAP training with a group of licensed clinicians, try sitting for each other as a practicum experience. Get enough doses to explore dosing for psychelytic and psychedelic effects. With oral administration, try different administration protocols (we will cover this later, but they include variables related to dissolving tablets, the amount of time the medicine is held in the mouth, and whether or not the medicine is then swallowed). Try using silence and then various soundtracks. Try journaling or talking immediately following the sessions. Learn the ins and outs of your experience with the medicines. Explore variables key to integration. Your clients will certainly have radically different experiences, but your own experiences will help you understand much more about their reference points.

CREATING COMMUNITY FOR OURSELVES

This book was built in part from a collection of documents and handouts I prepared for the therapists in the *Ketamine Kollaborations* practicum/training program. It is an effort to offer up practical, how-to information in a consolidated way. This is offered, however, only as a foundation in a rapidly evolving field. The psychedelic-assisted psychotherapy world is going to see lots of movement and change in the coming decade. To stay in the loop in this field means to commit to a community of KAP practitioners.

In Philadelphia, my colleague set up a monthly meeting and listserv of KAP practitioners in our area—medical, clinical, and otherwise. We meet monthly, usually virtually, and sometimes at one of our offices/facilities. We welcome new members monthly. Sometimes we have a planned topic, but more often we are just chatting, letting one another know what we are doing, and asking questions in the meeting and in the chat. We share resources in the meeting and over the listserv. We reach out to each other individually or to the group for specific questions.

We and our clients all survived our clinical internships back in graduate school because we formed a community of learners. We were actively engaged in education and collaboration while getting our feet wet with the work. We were talking about our cases, asking questions, and reading material applying to our new clients. As uncomfortable as it might be to have to try a new thing in the room with our clients, we have successfully done this before. And community is the key variable.

Find out who is doing work in your area. Get on the national listserv, *Big Tent*. Start going to trainings, conferences, and retreats, in your area whenever possible. And if there isn't a community of practitioners in your area, start a monthly group. If you build it, they will come.

Preparing the Client

Given the current buzz about psychedelic-assisted psychotherapies, many of your friends, colleagues, acquaintances, current clients, and potential clients will be curious about your ketamine-related offerings. Both socially and professionally, many folx will be interested in exploring the option of psychedelic treatment for themselves. You will find yourself in countless paid and unpaid conversations discussing this treatment option. There is, however, a very steep climb between interest in and readiness to move forward with ketamine-assisted psychotherapy. Even among those who contact us professionally with the stated intention of doing KAP, most will not proceed with treatment. Among those who do proceed with KAP, the journey from interest to treatment may well be traveled at a snail's pace.

Despite the excitement and interest in psychedelics as a tool for healing, potential clients frequently bring much ambivalence. While excited by the possibilities, they also carry anxiety and uncertainty. Folx often have an overwhelming number of questions and a high desire for reassurance. They have people in their lives whom they need to get on board, potentially including their therapists and psychiatrists. Treatment requires a fairly significant financial and time investment. Some clients come to us more interested in MDMA or mushrooms, either because they have familiarity from prior experiences, or, in the case of mushrooms, because of an idealization of plant medicine, or because whatever great Netflix series they watched didn't cover ketamine.

A fair amount of clinical time and work is often required to help clients feel ready to participate in KAP. These are the steps:

EVALUATION

In the interest of time management, I do not engage in any conversation about KAP treatment with a client until I have emailed them some basic information about ketamine, KAP, and steps in my intake process. The essential element in this email is a link to an intake form as the first evaluation tool for candidacy. While the intake form can't rule a client in, it can definitely rule a client out.

The main goal of the initial intake form is to identify specific medical and psychological contraindications. These may eliminate the option of KAP, or simply dictate parameters like dosage, frequency, or location of medicine sessions. Based on the answers, I might end my evaluation and email or discuss with the client other treatment options.

The initial intake form gathers other information pertinent to further evaluation and preparation for KAP. It includes the option of providing signed releases for conversations with their other mental health providers. It alerts me to a history of trauma, prior experiences with psychedelics, goals for treatment, and the like. This information will help direct the initial consultation.

I offer a free 20-minute introductory consultation to further assess if an interested person is an appropriate candidate and a good match for my particular services. (See "Who Is and Isn't a Good Candidate" for more information.) This means I spend quite a few unpaid hours that may or may not yield paid services. Even good candidates don't always proceed with treatment. As psychedelic-assisted psychotherapy becomes a bit more familiar, an increasing percentage of our initial consultations will lead to a client choosing KAP. In these early years, these emails/intakes/evaluations/conversations are at least partly in the service of building social familiarity with psychedelic-assisted psychotherapies.

MANAGING EXPECTATIONS

Clients come to KAP, sometimes with excitement and expectations, sometimes with fears that it may be a futile effort, but all because they have a hope that it might help them resolve some of their core suffering. Efforts to help our clients manage realistic expectations need to be woven into all intake and preparations sessions.

Partly driven by my desire to provide the client enough excitement-fuel to move them through general ambivalence about this new treatment, I am inclined to share my enthusiasm about what a helpful tool ketamine and KAP can be for treating entrenched mental health dilemmas. Not only from the research, but from experience with clients, friends, colleagues, and my ketamine experiences as a client, I know this medicine, when taken in the context of therapy, can frequently dislodge people from profoundly stuck places. As a psychotherapist who has worked with stuck clients for decades, I suspect my excitement can be palpable. The problem is that it doesn't always work.

The medicine not working is an absolute possibility. What "not working" means can vary, but there are plenty of times when clients are deemed candidates, do a trial of ketamine and/or KAP, and it simply does not help. Prior to asking clients to commit their hopefulness to this expensive and time-consuming round of treatments, here are three possible outcomes we want them to have considered:

- Treatment-Resistant Depression: Ketamine, when taken with a specific protocol, separate from any participation in psychotherapy, can alleviate symptoms of depression in two thirds of people with treatment-resistant depression. That means one third will not have their symptoms alleviated by the medicine. It is essential that clients are well aware of this possibility. The significance of this information is magnified by the desperation among people with treatment-resistant depression. They have already had many failed treatments and likely struggle around themes of hopefulness and hopelessness. We need to make sure they absolutely understand this before beginning a course of treatment so as to not set them up for terrible disappointment. They will likely be terribly disappointed if the treatment does not help alleviate their symptoms, but we don't want it to be because we supported unrealistic expectations.

- Medicine Mismatch: Some clients will not be able to successfully use the medicine. It might give them headaches or nausea or leave them groggy, and those might be reasons they don't want to continue treatment. They may find the experience itself unpleasant in a way that discourages them from pursuing further medicine sessions. Some clients, despite high medicine dosages, cannot access a psychedelic experience. We need to warn clients that only trial and error will help us figure out if it will work or how it will work for them.

- Not a Magic Treatment: Ketamine medicine sessions have a high probability of facilitating an experience of epiphany/revelation/rebirthing/awakening. Would that epiphany might be enough to heal what ails us! While these profound experiences can be used to leverage real and sustainable change, prospective clients need to understand that it will require effort. As with any wonderful moment of realization we may have in life, our job is to unpack that new data, rework our understanding based on it, and learn how to integrate the learnings into our lives. While there is something a bit magical about ketamine and psychedelic experiences, they do not eliminate the need to do ongoing therapy work to build those epiphanies into our approach to living.

Supporting enough enthusiasm in our clients to try this novel treatment while helping them keep expectations in check is a balance worth seeking.

ADDRESSING FEARS

Many clients interested in psychedelic-assisted psychotherapy bring some fears, uncertainties, and concerns to their early evaluation and preparation sessions. Prospective KAP clients may or may not have experience with psychedelics, other mood- or mind-altering substances, or non-ordinary states achieved through meditation or breath techniques. Some will come with prior experiences with psychedelics that were bad, which may lead to some hesitancy and nervousness about this treatment. All will have important questions about both the medicine itself and the medicine experience.

Some of the work of preparing the client is to address their fears. There are some qualities to ketamine that make this a particularly safe medicine, medically, psychologically, and experientially:

Medically

The medicine itself is exceedingly safe, tried and tested, in hospitals and outpatient medical settings for decades, with young and old alike. It has minimal risks and side effects, has few conflicts with other medications, and is very short acting. As long as clients do not suffer from the counter-indicated conditions of untreated heart or high-blood pressure conditions, it is a particularly safe medication. Working with a known prescriber can help you in your efforts to assure clients medically, as you will be able to trust differently in their assessment.

Psychologically

A benefit of psychedelics is that they help people detach from default-mode thinking. That detachment includes dismantling false certainties and internal scaffolding that is part of what we seek to change. It can be somewhat destabilizing and disorienting. Again, that is partly the goal. But we want to know if people have reality-testing capacity and skills for grounding and orienting themselves.

I do not work with clients with symptoms of schizophrenia, paranoid or delusional thinking, serious bouts of destructive mania, pervasive dissociative disorders or dissociative identity disorder, significant borderline tendencies, or any client I deem to have a loose grasp on reality and organized cognitive functioning. Some practitioners specialize in some of these conditions, or are more experienced with KAP, who may offer services to these populations, but I do not. Some of these prospective clients might be served by some of the other psychedelic offerings as they become available. Because I eliminate clients with psychological risks for this treatment, I can confidently tell my prospective clients that this is a safe medicine.

Another psychological safety concern for the client is fear of a "bad trip." When a client shares this concern, and most do, I first explore with them what they mean by a bad trip:

- Uncomfortable access to their own material? Fear of being trapped in a nightmare of sorts?

- Fear of ego dissolution or ego death, or some other surreal experience they fear will frighten them?

- Worried about the session itself or afraid they won't be able to shake the experience?

- Frightened by the loss of control or disconnection from reality?

- Fixated on practical components, like the taste of the medicine, or fear they will need to urinate?

Here are some responses to fears, questions, and anxieties about the medicine session experience:

- Short-Lasting Experience: Anxiety around bad trips is often linked to fears of being trapped in a frightening state for an extended period of time. Ketamine medicine sessions typically last only about 40 minutes.

- Difficult Material: In almost every case, even if the session is difficult, the material will ultimately be meaningful and useful, perhaps offering keys and clues to the very issues plaguing them. They are bringing to the medicine the wish for healing, not just a good time, and sometimes healing requires going into hard places.

- Dissociative Quality: This particular medicine creates an experience of some distance or space between the client and their experience. It enables an observing ego that can connect to the material that is surfacing, but with some separation that feels quite containing.

- Trauma Work Isn't Always Traumatic: Even for clients who have an intention to work on aspects of trauma, it does not mean the work is going to be traumatic. The medicine may take them on a journey of joy, meant to show them freedom from trauma.

- Overall Sense of Well-Being: Most who take this medicine describe an overall sense of well-being and "okayness," even when the material they are contemplating would otherwise be unsettling. This is in large part due to the anesthetic and dissociative qualities of the medicine.

- Low-Dose Protocols: For clients with significant concerns or anxieties about having a bad medicine experience, I strongly recommend starting them at a lower dose to become comfortable with the experience. We would likely prioritize live medicine sessions with the therapist. Preparation with this client would likely be extended to include a more collaboratively developed plan for how to help the client feel safe and contained in the medicine session.

- Short-Lasting Effects: Much like a dream, a medicine session experience quickly fades unless captured in conversation or journaling immediately following the experience. Affect may linger, but it is typically much diluted.

Addressing clients' fears and concerns isn't just to get them ready for the treatment: it is part of the treatment. Sometimes we are grappling with a client's general anxious approach to all things, in which case we may need to encourage them to just get started with low-dose protocols. If it is fear/concern-based, however, there is no need to rush to get to medicine sessions.

Experientially

Clients will be interested in a rundown of what will happen during medicine sessions. As the clinician in the room, part of the appeal for me of ketamine in particular is its anesthetic effects. Rarely is a client going to want to get up, walk around, dance, try to take their clothes off, go outside, hug me, or any of the other types of active body experiences possible and probable with most psychedelics. While clients may sit up or remove their eye masks, the medicine encourages a passive body, with a focus on the internal experience.

Other frequent concerns about physical experience are around nausea and urination. I encourage clients to stop eating two to three hours before the medicine session and stop drinking an hour before. Their prescriber will prescribe anti-nausea medicine to take before the session. I recommend they use it the first couple of times, and then they can decide if they want to try a session without it. As per needing to urinate, that may well happen. We will encourage them to use the restroom right before taking the medicine. We will explain how we would go about supporting them to get to the bathroom if they end up needing it.

The other concern that arises is how they will get home after the session if they have done it live in our office. Regardless of how they feel, driving themselves, or really even taking public transportation, is not a safe option. They will need to have arranged transportation.

SET AND INTENTION

"Set and Setting" is a commonly used phrase in the psychedelic world. Set is a reference to the client's mind**set** as they prepare for and enter the medicine session. Setting refers to the physical space and the context of the medicine session. The therapist is largely responsible for providing a setting conducive to KAP. Set, however, is co-constructed between client and therapist in the preparation sessions prior to each medicine session. Here are some elements related to helping clients prepare their mindset for a fruitful experience:

Timing Matters: Before beginning with KAP, I encourage clients to consider their larger life circumstances, so they might select a conducive time in their lives to do this deep dive. To reap the most rewards from KAP, they will need to establish and maintain a therapeutic focus for several months, honing their treatment intentions weekly. Because we are also seeking to capitalize on the increased neuroplasticity, these months will be filled with homework assignments, habit-formation activities, behavioral change efforts, journaling and conversation assignments, etc. This treatment isn't meant to be squeezed into one's life. It is a main event.

Reverence: While KAP is squarely centered in the clinical therapeutic world, it is best experienced nestled in the world of sacred ceremony. Religious and spiritual frameworks aside, entering a psychedelic state should be an event. We increase its potency, usefulness, and readiness for the work of integration by treating it as special, out of the ordinary, and worthy of ongoing mental/physical/emotional attention.

Intention Setting: Essential to a fruitful medicine session is a clear intention. One way to frame the opportunity psychedelics provide is to create a dialogue between our conscious and unconscious selves. Prior to each medicine session, the client's conscious and unconscious selves can be encouraged to contemplate the wish/hope/goal/question/intention they will be bringing to that dialogue. Because the development of clear intentions is central to successful

KAP work, and because that focus requires time to hone, I introduce the idea of intentions in all my first points of contact with prospective clients.

Homework: As an analytically oriented psychotherapist, I have deep reluctance to do anything that smells of homework/concrete assignments—except as it relates to KAP. Prior to medicine sessions, the work clients do at home will help with their intentions and awaken their unconscious to the upcoming dialogue. After medicine sessions, the goal includes use of the neuroplasticity available in the days following each medicine session. We ask clients to journal in order to establish a strong connection to their material and their unconscious mind. We encourage them to engage in conversation, spend time in nature, make art, listen to music, engage in prayer, stretch their body, and pay attention to what they are eating. They have an opportunity to change the way their brain handles/responds to/experiences/understands data: homework is useful fodder.

Week of/Day of Preparation: The last element of mindset is about the days and hours before the medicine sessions. We are asking our clients to care about their mindset, entering their session focused, rested, nourished, thoughtful. I send them instructions on some basic do's and don'ts before the first medicine session. As they understand how the medicine works in their system, they will develop their own rituals for preparing to enter the psychedelic realm.

TRUST, LET GO, BE OPEN

Besides specific intentions that clients develop for each of their medicine sessions, it is helpful for both client and clinician to keep in mind some more general intentions as well. "Trust, let go, be open" is another common phrase associated with psychedelics that can operate as an intention of sorts at multiple points in the medicine session.

There is a reason psychedelic experiences are often referred to as trips and journeys. Most people experience a fair amount of movement while using psychedelics: sometimes being blown gently by wind, or traveling down rivers, flying above landscapes, or floating in outer space. Visuals frequently accompany the experience and those visuals transform in perspective from telescopic to microscopic, multidimensional, and shape-shifting objects. Thoughts, including a well-developed intention, can evolve, digress, disappear, or otherwise transform.

During the medicine sessions, clients can feel overwhelmed, disoriented, or confused. Sometimes the client is seeking direction. Telling themselves to "trust, let go, be open" is a great way to gently guide their own session. A primary goal of the actual medicine session is to allow the unconscious to take the lead. This mantra of sorts can be used to help clients get their conscious mind out of the way.

So much of our work as KAP clinicians is centered on holding space and being as non-directive as we can. Encouraging clients to go with the flow, and follow their unconscious where it leads them, is pretty much the most directive we get.

INNER HEALING WISDOM

Another part of the well-established lingo in the psychedelic field is references to Inner Healer and Inner Healing Wisdom. While, as a clinician, I am more inclined to use the language of the unconscious, the phrase "Inner Healing Wisdom" has a lovely feel to it and is ultimately what we are asking the medicine to help us access. I offer this language to clients to help them develop a relationship with the parts of themselves that seek truth and healing.

For some of our clients, it will take convincing that their truth lies inside them, and that ultimately they are the best guide out of their suffering. Part of the wonder of psychedelic-assisted psychotherapy is for clients to trust a hard lean into the possibility that we hold the wisdom for our healing.

SETTING FOR SESSIONS AND INTEGRATION

In its most basic sense, setting is a reference to the physical environment in which the client does their medicine session. This may be our offices, their homes, infusion centers, or retreat settings, and includes all the details related to how that space is furnished. In a more clinical sense, setting is also the holding environment, or safe container, in which our clients will do their medicine journeys.

I think it is worth extending our concept of "setting" to include the larger community in which we and our clients will do KAP and to participate in efforts to make that larger setting a safer container. While they are doing this deep dive into their unconscious, they will be living and conversing with their partners, friends, family, and colleagues, other mental health providers, their larger social networks, and will be subjected to society's wide-ranging views on both psychedelics and therapy. As clinicians offering a new treatment model with a fair amount of associated stigma and fear, we can serve our clients well by tending to the safety of their larger settings.

Their Clinical Team

While individual medicine sessions may be illuminating and even healing for clients, the lasting work is in integration. Medicine sessions offer the opportunity to have a dream that illuminates new paths and elements for healing. The other members of their team will be carrying the flame alongside us, if it is our client, or long after their work with us if we offered KAP as a complementary therapy. We must keep their team in the loop enough to transfer the flame.

Outpatient Therapist: When offering KAP to our own clients, longstanding or new, we are likely the central figure in their treatment team. Just as often, KAP is part of a complementary treatment to the client's ongoing psychotherapy work with another clinician. Whether the client was referred by the client's primary therapist or came to us by another means, their primary therapist is still the central figure in their team. It is essential we integrate their therapist into the work. This means consultation before, during, and after our work with their client.

The clinical relationship in a long-term ongoing psychotherapy cannot be matched by short-term KAP treatment. The client's therapist's familiarity with the client's internal terrain is essential data for helping the client develop intentions for each medicine session, for assisting us in understanding what they might encounter during the medicine session, and ultimately for the ongoing work of integration that the client will be doing with their therapist.

We know something about the psychedelic tool and how to leverage it. It benefits the client for us to impart as much of this to their therapist as possible. I offer clinicians both consultation opportunities for general overview and Q&A to discuss ketamine and KAP, or consultations to collaborate about their client in particular. In my business model, for an overview, the therapist pays for the consultation, and if it is client specific, the client pays.

Clinical Team: For clients who have other clinicians who are part of their treatment team, like couples, group, or family therapists, or therapists offering complementary services like EMDR or somatic therapies, it is worth encouraging the client to keep those providers in the loop. KAP has the potential to be a real game changer and will surely be noteworthy as a reference point for the work they are doing with other clinicians. I offer the same consultation services to all members of their team.

Psychiatrist: If the client has an existing psychiatrist, I strongly encourage them to keep their psychiatrist in the loop. While this may seem like a given, many clients do not want to share their interest in psychedelics with what they imagine is an old-school, conservative psychiatrist. They may indeed be correct that their psychiatrist disapproves of this treatment. It is also highly likely that, even if the psychiatrist supports the treatment, they won't serve as the prescriber. Nevertheless, it is still important to include them in this conversation.

For the client, it is important, because this is a big event in their treatment life. Their providers should at least be informed if not acting as decision makers. This arrangement can obviously go wrong. Some psychiatrists will successfully convince their clients not to proceed, despite a lack of contraindications. Some psychiatrists will refuse to work with the client if the client proceeds with KAP treatment. But, as clinicians, I feel we cannot participate in supporting clients keeping key information away from their providers.

As KAP providers, there is an additional motivation to encourage the client to loop their psychiatrists into conversations about ketamine: It is this kind of exposure, and these kinds of conversations, that are going to increase the visibility and acceptability of psychedelic treatments. And, as a bonus, we might find they are willing to be a prescriber for their client and perhaps our clients as well.

Partners/Family/Friends

We know as therapists how supportive, unsupportive, or downright undermining family and friends can be in our clients' efforts in therapy. In the case of psychedelic-assisted psychotherapy, a couple of factors make it extra important that clients either get their people on board or are prepared to insulate/protect themselves from potential naysayers or critics.

The first issue is the stigma and misconceptions about psychedelics, ketamine in particular, and their relationship to therapy and healing. Our clients will likely be faced at a minimum with a lot of questions and potentially some pushback. We need to arm them with information, statistics, articles, and ideas to educate their community of friends and family.

The other significant variable is that psychedelics act as an intense accelerator to psychic work. Our clients, and the people closest to them, benefit from being prepared for big changes in how the client feels and thinks about themselves, their lives, their work, their relationships, etc. While it is best practice for us to caution clients about making big decisions early on in their treatment, much like for people in early drug and alcohol recovery, they may find themselves wanting to have very different conversations with the people around them. Everyone is best served by being prepared for that.

The Larger Community/Society

Even before I introduced KAP into my practice, I spent a ridiculous amount of time offering free consulting hours to potential clients, their families, and their clinical team. In part, it is an ethical practice related to a belief in applying consumership principles to our field. Clients should know something about who we are and what we offer before being expected to pay for our services. But it is also a business practice strategy aimed at engaging potential and future clients.

In the case of my KAP practice, increased overall familiarity in our larger communities with the role psychedelics can play in healing will improve accessibility for everyone. I see my free consulting hours as public relations efforts for this new, potentially transformational therapy tool. These efforts will both improve my own chances for a successful KAP practice as well as promote a safer environment for my clients to do their work.

PART THREE

CONCLUSION: INTEGRATION

You are considering starting a new journey with your work and practice. We are discussing clients considering a novel treatment. Moving these journeys to fruition will require engaging with lots of newness. The goal of incorporating KAP into your practice, or for the client considering a series of KAP treatments, is to later arrive at a new familiar, a better familiar, a richer familiar.

Integration for the Client

People often tell stories about their aunt who received a life-threatening diagnosis and used it to manifest gratitude in her everyday life, or the parent whose gay child didn't include them in their wedding and it inspired them to build a bridge back to that relationship, or the person who traveled to some faraway land and encountered abject poverty and returned to fight societal poverty in their country of origin. It can happen, a few times in our lives, that we have an experience that awakens a drive for radical change in our lives. Unfortunately, more commonly, even profound realizations fail to yield any significant changes in our daily lives over the long haul.

As a tool, ketamine can exponentially increase access to profound experiences of revelation/epiphany. The medicine quiets the mind, brings core unconscious and/or existential themes to the surface, lowers the defenses, and provides a fluid mind to assemble a new perspective on oneself/life/relationships/beliefs/understanding. But the revelation/epiphany is only the beginning. It is the work of integration that provides successful, sustainable change.

STRUCTURE OF TREATMENT

As previously laid out in some detail, there are many ways to structure our client's treatment. The dosing and frequency protocols, as well as the setting of the medicine sessions, impact how integration unfolds as well.

Antidepressant Protocols

When a client is using an antidepressant protocol for KAP, they often do one or two medicine sessions a week for two to three months because of the possibility of symptom improvement from the medicine itself with this protocol. The frequency of sessions provides some unique opportunities for integration as well as some barriers.

The best way to enter medicine sessions is with a clear, simple, well-formulated intention. To be able to formulate specific, appropriate, and relevant intentions once or twice a week requires some commitment and focus. Typically, we are building on previous medicine sessions to help us hone our next session's focus. This means scheduling lots of dual-purpose preparation/integration sessions on either side of each medicine session in which we help the client ascertain the material from their last session and use it to build the next intention.

With once- or twice-a-week protocols, we are also looking at weeks of ongoing heightened mental flexibility that leads to new ideas/understandings/connections. In using such an intensive protocol, we want to support our client to take full advantage of this opportunity with writing prompts, time in nature, conversation with friends, meditation, art, and thoughtful books/TV/movies/podcasts.

Occasionally we will have clients only interested in the antidepressant effects of the medicine. They may let the use of the medicine session experience and the neuroplasticity in the days that follow remain untapped. Many people in the world are looking for quick and easy fixes, and ketamine can indeed often provide relief without the effort of psychological work. But if we have a client interested in the intensive ketamine protocol, it behooves us to encourage them to treat that two- to three-month protocol period with a focused curiosity and heightened devotion to insight-oriented change and growth.

Before starting an intensive protocol, I encourage clients to choose a two- to three-month period when their mental health and well-being can be one of their primary focuses. Their therapeutic work and goals should be the first and last things on their minds as they get out of and into bed. The day should include activities focusing on self-exploration and new narratives. It is a rare opportunity in life to have consistent access to intentional lucid dreaming (the medicine sessions), and the mental flexibility of a child (the resulting neuroplasticity). It is a most wondrous opportunity.

Client/Clinician/Theme-Driven Pacing

If our client does not need to access the specific antidepressant benefit of the medicine, we are free to develop frequency protocols as we go. We may start out with once every week or two, or monthly sessions. We may do relatively few sessions, waiting for very specific material to surface that could benefit from the assistance of the medicine. We may only do a handful of sessions to help open the client to a new narrative or perspective. We may use the medicine only to work on very specific material, perhaps trauma work. As clinicians, we are at choice with our clients to devise and adjust our treatment protocols to best suit our individual practice and our clients' needs.

The medicine brings a lot of material to the surface to be processed. It can easily bring up too much material. One session could easily provide enough material for processing during a month of therapy. The medicine also produces an experience that must be metabolized. Experiences of expansiveness, of connection, of self-love, all need time to process, digest, and make part of the self. Clients may be taking the medicine once every month or two only when a particular intention is well formulated and developed, or when a previous session's material feels well understood and operationalized in the client's life.

Integration is our guiding star, or true north. Successful integration is the goal around which we establish and modify our treatment protocols. While people can have lovely experiences on the medicine, seeing our clients successfully use the medicine sessions and neuroplasticity of the mind to make changes in their life is the barometer for the effectiveness of this tool.

SEASONS OF INTEGRATION

Integration isn't an act or even a set of steps. It has many faces and reveals itself at many junctures along life's many paths.

At the Start of KAP Work

To take ketamine-assisted psychotherapy seriously, we want our clients focused on using the medicine sessions and neuroplasticity to their full advantage. This is not a medicine to be taken passively. We want our clients committed to being proactive/reactive/active.

After the first couple of sessions, we want to look for how the client is treating the process and if they are treating the surfacing material with proper care and attention. We want them thinking/talking/writing/creating about their experience in the days that follow each session. We want to see them working on creating and untangling new "aha" moments in the days between sessions.

Integration first requires metabolization; grappling with material, turning it over in our minds, playing it against other ideas, noting our bodies' reactions to our thoughts. This is the work we are asking our clients to do between sessions. This active process of percolating/digesting/mulling over/fermenting must be happening in direct connection to the medicine session.

If they are experiencing rich medicine session journeys but then can't really find a way to think about the material or make use of the somatic experience of the medicine sessions in preparation and integration sessions, it is worth taking note if this treatment tool is a good match with the client. Integration of the medicine session is key to long-term improvement for our clients. If they are unable to make some meaning with us about the sessions, we might slow down the use of ketamine and reevaluate its usefulness with that particular client.

If we have a client who comes to each session prepared to connect the last session to the current and then to the next, along with thoughts/conversations/readings/activities of the week, then we have someone who is actively engaging with this treatment model and integrating material as they go. This is the ideal. We may not get the ideal, but we definitely want to see rich engagement.

Over the Months

People bring hopes of radical, fundamental, core change to psychedelic-assisted psychotherapy. More often than not, clients are offered opportunities for that radical change during their KAP treatment. This is both the good news and the hard news.

Big, fast dismantling of internal systems for understanding the self/life/relationships/childhood, etc., can be quite destabilizing and disorienting. If KAP successfully helps them topple an arcane internal world, they will have an opportunity to rebuild their approach to life and living. Most clients have come to us because they feel stuck. Unstuck is great, but it can also be bumpy.

Besides general disorientation and destabilization, the somatic experiences, unconscious revelations, and all the ways that our clients unpack their experiences with ketamine during the months of treatment and post-treatment, sometimes bring very daunting material to the surface. Ketamine offers our clients opportunities to see things about themselves/lives/relationships/world/world-view anew, with some clarity and emotional honesty. What they see might be hard for them. The hardest parts of the process may become the very beacon for the next chapter of their life's work.

We ask clients not to make hasty decisions in the early months of KAP work, much like 12-step programs that ask the same of those entering recovery. It takes time to integrate new ideas and concepts with old understanding and frames. Sometimes, the new and the old don't seem to fit well. Clients can want to ditch jobs and partners or make other massive life changes because of revelations about their current life. But sometimes, the next set of revelations will lead them to alter rather than eliminate certain facets of their lives. Clients are often surprised about how much change they can leverage in seemingly stuck situations with a new mindset.

In the months during and proceeding a series of KAP treatments, we should expect to see some significant shifts inside our clients. Our clients may be very aware of their shifts in thinking/mood/understanding, unaware of any changes at all, or unable to describe what feels different. As the clinician in the room, we should be looking for observable change. It might look/feel subtle or nuanced, but we should be looking for meaningful internal shifts. KAP isn't trying to help a client resolve a little issue here or there. It offers clients an opportunity to step out of their world-view, in mind/thought and body/soma. With their defenses lowered, they gain access to the wisest parts of themselves and their unconscious. If KAP is "working," we will be able to see it in our clients' mood/perspective/understanding/relationships/life over the months following a series of treatments.

Over the Years

As clinicians, one of the hardest truths we face is that change takes time. Even worse is that the drive for change ebbs and flows, and so sometimes our clients are hardly even working toward it. Same with KAP: some clients make great use of it, and some, a lot less so. Sometimes the work moves smoothly; other times less so. Sometimes the fruits of our labor are abundant; other times, there is little edible fruit.

And then, suddenly, much later, a harvest reveals itself. Sometimes the work our clients are doing is unconscious and underground even to them. Whether thwarted, slow moving, happening in bursts, or at a steady, digestible rate, the integration of material our clients access through KAP will continue to contribute to their building a good life long after our work together. As a clinician who commonly works with clients for over a decade at a time,

I know that all we learn in life we must relearn and review over and over. This is so we might reorganize and re-metabolize it with all the new ways we have grown. In some ways, integration is another word for living.

EVIDENCE/SIGNS/TYPES OF INTEGRATION

Clients come to us with a range of goals and intentions for their work with ketamine. Some are hoping to see or think or feel differently about a particular situation. Some are looking for a way forward with a behavior, set of thoughts, or a situation. Some are hoping to bring a concrete change into their lives, with others leaning more toward wanting to see a path/opening of sorts.

Concrete Changes

The neuroplasticity offered by ketamine in the days immediately following each medicine session creates near ideal conditions for concrete change. If your client is hoping to alter/add/eliminate particular behaviors/thoughts/patterns, the days immediately following each medicine session are a highly productive time for pairing with therapeutic homework assignments.

As mentioned earlier, I am generally averse to anything resembling homework in therapy. I typically refer a client seeking homework to a therapist better equipped to work within that model. However, even if concrete isn't your thing as a clinician or client, it is a waste not to use the available neuroplasticity to the client's advantage. Creating a plan for how the client will use the days between medicine sessions is essential to solid KAP work.

If clients have specific behaviors they hope to start implementing in their lives, the days immediately following each medicine session are ripe for change. We will ask our clients to engage in some combination of relevant behaviors: mindfulness/meditation, journaling, reaching out to friends, walking in the woods, movement, hard conversations, self-care activities, eating well, getting to work on time, etc.

They may or may not be successful at doing these activities, but they are likely to have new thoughts and feelings and associations related to their efforts. My main gripe about homework in therapy is that it is almost predictably a set-up for failure. Nothing will magically resolve itself in response to the medicine session or the neuroplasticity. The reason we want our clients to try these homework assignments is not just so they might build new habits, but because neuroplasticity will help shine new light on their internal conflict.

Some KAP clients will be able to track successfully concrete changes in their lives. For others, those changes will remain out of reach. We well understand as therapists that the roads we traverse to a better life are rarely easy or straight. A failure to implement concrete changes in response to KAP does not mean the treatment was a failure. There are less obvious changes we are also tracking.

Mood Disorders

For clients seeking help with mood from their KAP treatment, the evidence can be mixed over the first few weeks. For clients seeking relief from depression in particular, it can easily take up to six to eight weeks to see if the medicine itself might help improve the client's depression. And for anxiety relief, the medicine may further dysregulate the client's mood before it potentially helps.

If the client does experience improvement in their mood that seems linked to the treatment-resistant depression protocol, after eight weeks or so, the client might stop doing regular ketamine sessions. Your prescriber can help you figure out if the client is responding to the medicine. If the medicine itself was positively impacting their mood, then we would expect every one to three months that they might see a dip in their mood requiring an occasional "booster" ketamine session.

One complication in the benefit analysis is that while they are using the medicine for mood improvement, they are also having medicine experiences and KAP. A mood improvement may be a response to the medicine itself but may also be the shifting of their internal narrative.

Another complication is that their mood might actually worsen for a while. The goal of medicine sessions is contact with core unconscious material. Our clients are entering a lucid dream to ask their inner wisdom to show them a path out of their suffering. Medicine sessions can be very disruptive to the mood because of the material that may surface. Even the most beautiful of epiphanies can be fraught with grief and pain. Change can be very uncomfortable.

But over time, evidence of successful treatment often manifests in a greatly improved mood. There are common targets for the tool of KAP, like shame, self-hatred, grief, trauma, all of which, if shifted, might radically improve mood over time. New understandings of the self are likely to lead to a client having a less critical self, improved capacity to take in good things, more expansive view, etc. Ketamine routinely offers people access to more spaciousness, internal freedom, improved self-esteem and confidence, increased agency, and all the makings of a more content human.

Overall Well-being

Ultimately, we want the kind of change for our clients that will result in a noticeable improvement in their condition. This may not look like a resolution of a mood disorder, and it may not usher in all the great behavioral changes our clients often seek. But over time, we want to see them wrestling differently with old conundrums, having increased awareness of themselves, feeling some spaciousness inside their system, experiencing curiosity for new ideas and thinking, challenging old assumptions, etc.

Similar to the discussion of impact on mood, the road to an overall improvement in well-being is usually quite bumpy. The improvement in well-being may include things like being more honest with themselves, which might mean spending some time with painful truths. The improvement may have lifted blocks to trauma, and our client might have to manage some months of new discovery and grief.

The current press about psychedelic-assisted psychotherapy promotes an idealized version of treatment. Neither ketamine nor KAP will "cure" your client nor eliminate their suffering nor even necessarily their need for continued treatment, including antidepressants. Ketamine and KAP are simply tools. The work of self-discovery, of learning how to leverage one's agency, of creating the life we want, is an ongoing process, without beginning or end. Grappling with suffering is a lifelong endeavor. We can get better or worse at it, but it will still exist. Personally, psychotherapy is one of my favorite tools for grappling with the hard stuff and finding/building the self/life I seek. KAP is now also among my top tools.

Integration for the Clinician

In the coming years, our clients may want to explore multiple psychedelics in their efforts toward healing. It is worth it for us to understand how to leverage all these medicines for real, sustained growth and well-being.

Some of you might have read this book to learn how to support clients in their work with other KAP providers. Some may want to offer this tool to a handful of your existing clients. Some may be shifting your practices to put KAP at the center of your professional lives. The good news is that all of these options can modify and grow with you over the years of your work.

Because this field is in such rapid growth, there are a plethora of ways to grow and evolve as a KAP clinician, integrate various elements into how you do your work, explore with whom and how you collaborate, and develop your specific approach to the work.

In my experience, evolving our work over the years is harder than getting started. As a group, clinicians tend to like to know how to do a thing before they have to do it. I experience us as people who don't speak another language out loud until we are proficient, who read up on how to place a bet at a racetrack before we get there so we can handle it seamlessly, and who read and watch "how-to" tutorials to avoid the missteps of failed first attempts.

But when we first became clinicians, we had to do the unthinkable. We had to sit in the room, in the role of the therapist, with an unsuspecting client, and simply proceed. While we might have tried our best to be as prepared as possible, the only real mastery in our field is born out of the hours we sit with clients, witnessing their lives and contemplating their truths.

Surprisingly, clients get immense benefit from their work with master's-level student clinical interns. The gaps and the glitches in the students' knowledge and technique do not deter positive outcomes. Our clients need a safe place to be heard, contained, and considered. The basics that college teachers and supervisors told us would be enough were indeed enough.

The same is true for our journey offering KAP. We will get better at evaluating clients, prepping them, managing their expectations, supporting them during medicine sessions, and helping them integrate the material. We will also get better at our procedures and paperwork and administration of our program. But we can start now. That is how we are going to build the additional strengths, understanding, and capacity. There is no other way forward than experience, in the room, with the clients, and, in this case, with this new tool.

PART FOUR

SNARKY OPINIONS

I am an exceedingly opinionated person and feel quite comfortable expressing my opinions in most settings. But, given the nature of a guidebook, it seemed this project was not a particularly appropriate venue for my snarky opinions. It was important to me that readers have available the standards and common practices in this emerging field. So, rather than eliminate my views from the book, I wanted to offer them in a sequestered way that allowed them to be taken for what they are: very strong opinions, delivered without as much careful professional packaging, but still only opinions.

Session Protocols

M uch of my divergence with some of the common standards in approach and perspective developing in the field of psychedelic-assisted therapy is connected to my entry point as a psychotherapist. The principles, approaches, steps, rituals, and guides for much of what we are calling "psychedelic-assisted psychotherapy" were neither designed nor are they always implemented by psychotherapists. Certainly many brave psychotherapists have been working underground to help develop treatment protocols and concepts for many decades. But psychotherapists were not the only professionals at the helm developing protocols for guided sessions.

MUSIC

Client use of some form of music during ketamine medicine sessions has become an industry standard. This is the best evidence to me that psychotherapists were not at the helm when treatment protocols were being established. Neither I nor any psychotherapist I know has ever curated or asked a client to curate a playlist to set and manage the mood for a therapy session. I would never imagine before a therapy session of any sort that I knew the topic, tone, or energy that would be a good accompaniment to the work my client and I were about to do.

One of my first classes in a program on healing with psychedelics focused on the use of music in medicine sessions. I found myself flooded and overwhelmed, thinking about the responsibility inherent in curating a playlist for my various clients' ketamine sessions. The teacher was lovely, talented, and knowledgeable. He talked about avoiding music with drumbeats, unless the goal was to help the client access anger. He reviewed how using unfamiliar music helped people access unfamiliar internal terrain, how familiar music might help ground a client who needed to go into a particularly dark place, and how vocals from male and female voices could elicit rich transferential or archetypal material. He described ways the therapist could curate a playlist, beginning with a slow building of intensity, then weaving in moments of sadness, exaltation, and longing, a crescendo for the height of the session, and then a taper down.

While riveted by this information, I was also flooded by thoughts of the overwhelming skill set I would need to learn to curate a soundtrack for my clients. I then realized my angst wasn't a response to all I would need to learn: my system was actually alerting me to a clash in clinical objectives.

The continuously declared stance of psychedelic-assisted psychotherapies is for the therapist to be as non-directive as possible. The essential position is that the medicine and the participant's inner healing wisdom are the guides, and it is crucial we don't influence or disrupt that wisdom.

There is little in this world as directive as music. We all use it in our lives to set or alter or improve or accentuate a mood. The idea that we, or the client, prior to the medicine session, would predetermine the mood we wanted to establish and facilitate through the ebbs and flows of the session is wholly and completely counterintuitive and counterproductive. It does not match anything we know as therapists about our job, which is to track, not create, the movement of thoughts/feelings/energy/soma/aliveness/tension/joy in each session.

With my own clients, I do not work with music. This isn't a punishment or denial of pleasure. I count on the medicine to provide relevant soundscapes, just as the medicine sometimes offers clients visuals behind their eye masks. There is a particular deliciousness to the quality of the silence when one is on ketamine. It can feel very containing. It is a supported way to be with the self. And that is the goal—to be with the self.

Every person I know who has done ketamine themselves has done it almost exclusively with music, and they have very strong reactions to my "no-music" stance. They insist the music is both lovely and useful. The best I can say to anyone who is eager to use this medicine to know more about themselves is to try silence. Try being with yourself. Try a handful of sessions without music, where you sit with your own thoughts and feelings, find your own mood, discover stillness, and be with yourself.

TOUCH

Similar to how my body alerted me to something being terribly amiss when it came to conceptualizing music in KAP work, I felt the same full-body activation when I heard presenters and KAP providers talk about the issue of touch. Discussions of the maneuvers providers dance through to determine if, when, where, what type, and how to offer and assess consent for touch during the ketamine session are elaborate and filled with angst about getting it wrong.

The concerns are legitimate enough. Psychedelic-assisted psychotherapy has established important protocols to help protect and support clients around touch. Providers discuss and plan for what touch options are available, like hand holding or arm rubbing, make plans for which types of touch clients might want during the session, sign consents around those agreements, and also agree that no additional touch options can be added once the client takes the medicine. In best practice, clinicians also do some touch-refusal exercises with clients in preparation sessions to practice turning down requests or stopping touch during the medicine session.

These protocol acrobatics to enable touch are warranted if we agree that touch is an essential part of the treatment. Some clinicians already offer various forms of touch in their work with clients, from hugs and handshakes to holding the client while they weep. For clinicians who already offer touch in their psychotherapy practice, it makes sense that touch would play a role in their work in KAP as well. What I find baffling is that offering touch as part of the KAP treatment protocol has become a standard, like music. It is so much a standard that many clinicians who do not use touch as part of their existing clinical practice are simply following suit.

Touch does not play a role in my approach to psychotherapy. For me, psychotherapy is a field of words. Our words often get misinterpreted, received differently than we hoped, become saturated with emotionality intended and unintended, and carry conscious and unconscious material in multiple layers. Despite all this, we have words available as the tool to unpack the communication in the room. In my approach, adding touch is flooding the narrative with the unnamed.

I understand touch can be a healing medium—a rich means of communicating care, love, and support. But there are many offerings we do not use in the consulting room. I have never prepared a meal for a client, which is one of my strongest pathways to love and healing in my private life. Our clients can use many experiences in life, touch among them, to heal. That doesn't translate into us needing to offer every vehicle for healing available to them. For some clients, it would be transformative for them to have a good friend in life, but most of us know we can not successfully or appropriately offer that. For some, they will experience deep healing if they have consensual sex with someone who loves and cares for them, but that someone certainly won't be us. For some, sitting by the ocean will be healing, but it doesn't mean we need to offer them sessions at the beach. Just because something is healing doesn't mean it belongs in the therapy frame.

One of the arguments for touch in the context of therapy and in psychedelic-assisted psychotherapy is that it can create conditions for a corrective emotional experience. My work seeks to help clients craft a life where they get their needs met outside the consulting room, not to satisfy those needs within the therapy relationship. As an analytically oriented psychotherapist, my work is to help clients contend with their losses, rather than try to inadequately replace their lost loved one. We cannot protect our clients from suffering. Offering clients momentary relief in the form of touch that they have difficulty accessing in their daily lives is not worth the relational complications and risks it introduces for me.

When I tell people in the psychedelic world that I do not offer touch in my work, they tell me how good and grounding touch feels for clients while on ketamine, much like they tell me how wonderfully music is experienced. I believe it. I also think floating in my hot tub would feel great on ketamine, and I might even try it. But I am using ketamine to do clinical work. Something feeling nice or interesting isn't a good enough reason. Even something that feels grounding or healing isn't necessarily good enough, if I can offer those things in a safer, cleaner way. I believe in the potency of words. I believe in the potency of silence and reverie. I believe in my ability to hold something and someone in my mind in a way that allows them to feel my care.

If you use touch in your normal outpatient practice and you feel like it has a solid clinical grounding, with minimal risk, then I suspect touch may make sense to you in the ketamine session. If you have clinical reasons why you do not use touch in your psychotherapy practice, it is worth a critical analysis before incorporating it into your KAP work.

TWO-PERSON PROTOCOL

Current Federal Drug Administration (FDA) trials with MDMA and psilocybin use a two-person protocol for working with clients during medicine sessions. Research trials frequently use two licensed clinicians or, alternatively, explore use of one licensed clinician and one trained "sitter." Some in the field are treating these models as a precedent for outpatient work with psychedelics, even when the medicine is ketamine.

I have no opinion about whether a two-person protocol is necessary when working with MDMA or psilocybin as I don't work with those medicines. I know multiple underground providers who feel safe and confident in their ability to work clinically with these medicines without a second person and they can articulate why. What I am addressing here is the presumed necessity of a two-person protocol for ketamine sessions.

This is important, because outside of a research setting, a two-person protocol could literally double the cost for clients. KAP is already barely financially feasible for most clients, much less those financially compromised. Psychedelic-assisted psychotherapies are already exceedingly expensive because of the amount of clinical time required for implementation. Before assuming two providers are required to be present, it is worth noting a couple reasons ketamine-specific treatment outside of research settings may not warrant a two-person protocol.

One reason a two-person protocol makes sense with other psychedelics is that the sessions last a long time—from five to ten hours. Clinicians would be hard pressed to stay fully psychologically present and hold space for clients for that many hours on their own. The psychedelic experience on ketamine, by contrast, lasts around 40 minutes, with the typical medicine session lasting two to three hours (to accommodate preparation, taking the medicine, and some basic integration work afterwards, while the person steadies themselves).

A quality specific to ketamine is that clients are physically disinclined to move. While using some of the other psychedelics, clients may want to get up, use their bodies, dance, hug everyone in the room, touch and smell objects, and go outside. Ketamine, by contrast, is a dissociative anesthetic. It hardly requires two people to manage an anesthetized client. We do not need to worry that the client will need to be physically contained or corralled. It is highly unlikely—as unlikely as it is in any regular psychotherapy session with a client.

As clinicians, we have spent many hours in rooms with clients doing hard, emotional work. We are perfectly fit to work with our KAP clients by ourselves.

Risk Management

AT-HOME USE

The most useful and productive practice for KAP medicine sessions is for therapist and client to be together for a live medicine session experience, in a well-designed clinical space, where the therapist can help with takeoff, landing, and the psychedelic flight itself. But many factors can prevent clients from being able to do some or all of their medicine sessions with a therapist present. As noted, cost can be a barrier for many, if not most, particularly when considering ongoing sessions. Other concerns include arranging safe transport after the medicine session, clinical anxieties or concerns, time management for clients taking the medicine multiple times a week for a treatment-resistant depression protocol, etc.

Opinions about at-home use range from seeing it as wildly dangerous and unethical to online ketamine monthly prescription programs that don't assume any involvement by a therapist in a client's use of ketamine. Arguments against at-home use often amounts to cautionary tales of a medicine we are otherwise presenting as safe. I feel strongly that we need treatment models that allow for the option of KAP medicine sessions to be done iin clients' own homes. Obviously the model could not be offered to all clients, but rather based on information from thorough evaluations and assessments. But the absence of an at-home use option reserves KAP for only very wealthy people.

As a rule, I am not worried about the safety of this medicine or the psychedelic experience it produces. However, having ketamine assessed as medically safe for at-home use does not eliminate the need for a clinical assessment for at-home use. If we have a reason to explore at-home use with one of our clients, we need to use preparation sessions to assess if it is physically and psychologically safe for a client to take this medicine without a therapist's direct supervision.

Physical Safety for At-Home Use

Ketamine is an exceedingly safe medication, except with a handful of people who have particular co-existing conditions that would rule them out. Ketamine has been commonly used as an anesthetic for short medical procedures for decades. The medicine has been proven safe for medically fragile patients such as infants, the elderly, pregnant women, and patients with wide-ranging medical compromises. When used for medical procedures, it is administered in significantly higher doses than in KAP; and because it is short acting, it may be given multiple times over the course of a medical procedure. The medicine has few negative side effects and does not pose interactive complications with most medical conditions or medicines, which is why it is such a commonly used anesthetic in the medical world.

Most KAP therapists aren't additionally licensed prescribers. If the prescriber we or the client works with has deemed them eligible for ketamine, we don't carry the burden of responsibility, legally or emotionally. I work with prescribers I trust to assess if this medicine is safe for the client. Because I like to use a model that allows clients to choose at-home sessions, at least some of the time, I exclusively work with prescribers willing to prescribe for at-home use.

Medical contraindications for ketamine use are predominantly heart and blood pressure conditions. While people with treated heart and blood pressure conditions may still be ruled in as candidates for this medicine, I personally do not work with these clients in my outpatient office, nor would I consider them candidates for at-home use. For clients with heart and blood pressure conditions who have been cleared for ketamine use, I would still encourage them to work with an infusion center or a facility that is medically outfitted.

Assuming clients do not have heart or blood pressure conditions, I am no more medically concerned about them taking ketamine in my office or in their homes than I am about them taking a Klonopin or Ativan when they are having an anxiety/panic episode. In an abundance of caution, I insist they have another adult in the home during at-home use. In my own practice, that adult might well be included in a group text exchange between me and the client before and after the medicine session for basic check-ins if it is one of their first medicine sessions at home. I will have sent that adult some basic information about what to expect. Most of these measures are to help the client and the other adult feel safe and supported despite the absence of any actual danger.

Psychological Safety and Comfort for At-Home Use

Just as I do not work with what I consider high-risk cases of people with heart and blood pressure conditions, I do not offer outpatient or at-home KAP services to people with a significant risk of a manic episode; who have a bipolar diagnosis; who are or have a close familial diagnosis of schizophrenia or schizoaffective disorder; or who show other signs of paranoid, delusional, or disorganized thoughts. The relevant psychological risks associated with ketamine are linked to these conditions. Some clinicians may choose to do KAP work with these populations despite the risks. I do not. There are other medicines that are better suited to different populations and other clinicians with more experience and specialized skill sets than I have. This rule eliminates the need for me to carry serious concerns about known risks for my work with my client.

There are other everyday psychological safety concerns clients and clinicians can have about this medicine. A primary one is fear of a "bad trip." This fear may be based on past experiences with psychedelics or the lack of experience with mood- and mind-altering substances. This fear isn't specific to at-home use but heightened when considering doing their medicine session without us present.

Here are some of fears and realities about the "bad trip":

- Length of Medicine Session: Some psychedelics produce long-lasting altered realities. If the medicine takes the client to an uncomfortable or scary place, they may well be there for many hours. That could indeed be very distressing. Even if the material is difficult, however, ketamine sessions are short.

- Risky Behaviors: A risk with most psychedelics is the choices and the actions of the person on the medicine. While using most psychedelics, people have hours of activity and decision making about activity that they will do while under the influence. They may want to dance, sing, hug, run outside, go for a drive, call up old friends, go swimming, and any number of things potentially risky for someone under the influence of this medicine. This very rarely happens on ketamine. Most people lie almost completely still during sessions, even if their mind and emotional self are quite active.

- "Bad" Is a Perspective: Sometimes "bad" is a reference to hard or difficult medicine sessions that may connect the client to some central, core truths. A "difficult" medicine session on ketamine is unlikely to be related to the medicine's properties itself. It is related to what the medicine brought to the person's consciousness. Indeed, they are taking the medicine to get access to that material. Sometimes that material is difficult or dark, complicated or confusing. But, like a bad dream, it holds clues to the roots of their suffering.

Multiple variables impact whether or not live or various at-home models for medicine sessions are indicated.

Initial Sessions: I am inclined to do at least the first two or three medicine sessions live. These sessions will familiarize the client with the medicine itself (including dosage), with the psychedelic experience, and will set a frame for how to approach the medicine session. These first sessions introduce the client to how to hone their intentions and mindset before the session, how to enter the journey mindfully while maintaining an internal focus, and how to return to a non-ordinary state thoughtfully.

Client Anxiety: Many clients will need to do initial sessions with us to manage general anxiety or manage their concerns about this treatment. Some of these clients will want and benefit from having us present at their medicine sessions. For some, the first few sessions will help them feel prepared to do the medicine on their own.

Familiarity with Non-Ordinary States: Some clients will feel open and interested in doing medicine sessions at home from the start if they have had previous psychedelic experiences. While I definitely prefer to do the first couple sessions with a client, I can be open to this if other considerations are more pressing (finances, social anxiety, transportation, etc.).

Trauma/PTSD: Trauma does not always present itself in ketamine sessions in scary or dark ways. Sometimes the most trauma-focused sessions look like the client accessing experiences of self-love or connecting to the goodness of the world. But when we or our client is nervous that their suffering may show itself in a scary or overwhelming way, we would likely do those sessions live. This could even be with a client who has done dozens of at-home sessions but suddenly needs to do a piece of darker work that they want support through.

Trust, Let Go, Be Open: This is a centrally important component of successful medicine session journeys. For some clients, home, alone, may feel like a safer, more reasonable environment. For some, we may need to provide multiple live sessions at various points in their KAP work to help them learn how to trust, let go, and be open.

Self-Care/Intentionality: Another variable in my assessment is the client's capacity for self-care. When a client has a difficult medicine session at home, their work is to comfort themselves and/or be comforted by their at-home adult companion, much like they would if they awoke from a bad dream. Their work is to try to journal or otherwise capture the dream, so they can bring it to therapy to unravel. In order for me to support a client doing at-home medicine sessions, I would need to know that they are capable of basic self-care and capable of maintaining heightened intentionality/focus/seriousness around this work.

I have lots of speculations about why many in the ketamine field are against at-home use as an available model. Cynically, I worry it is an economically driven strategy, as three-hour medicine sessions are profit-friendly. I absolutely believe in getting paid for my work, and I think the best model for practice, at least in most cases, is live, with your therapist. I just also understand that most people do not have the financial and time resources to make that a reasonable treatment option. And this medicine is way too valuable as a tool to reserve it for the handful of people who can afford a live-only model.

Cynicism in check, the main concern driving KAP therapists is about client safety with this new tool. I think each practitioner benefits from an honest reckoning with themselves about their concerns and assessing if 1) those concerns are applicable to all their clients; and 2) if there might be a way to create an at-home model that addresses their concerns while making this medicine and treatment tool available to eligible candidates who have barriers to exclusively in-office sessions.

It has surprised me how angst-filled and precautionary tales can dominate the narrative in KAP education and professional conversations. A central but always elusively vague fear from clinicians considering providing KAP is that an emergency situation will happen in their offices, medical or psychological, they will be alone to manage it, and it will additionally leave them in some sort of legal risk.

Rather than harmless fretting, fear of legal repercussions impacts if and how clinicians offer this important and exciting treatment to their clients. Many clinicians, despite great interest in KAP, will forgo pursuing it professionally for fear there will be no way to cover themselves legally from this vague, unnamed threat. For those of us already in the field, it can look like needlessly elaborate consent forms, access-limiting protocols like not supporting at-home use or not working with certain clients, and fear-phantasies of legal scenarios threatening our professional lives.

COVER YOUR ASS

I support protecting ourselves and our practice licenses in all circumstances. While I appreciate the brave psychotherapists out there offering underground psychedelic-assisted psychotherapy to bring healing to their clients, I work only with legal medicine under legal parameters. Given that, I am not particularly worried that my ass needs extra coverage. When we provide KAP as therapists, what we are providing is therapy. We have licenses and malpractice insurance for our work as therapists. These are a handful of reasonable additional precautions to implement to address some KAP-specific needs:

- Professional Collaboration: Develop a relationship with your prescriber and compounding pharmacy so that you and your clients and in good hands.

- Consent Forms: Research and create solid consent forms specific to your KAP practice. This is another reason it is good to have collaborators and to participate in the larger KAP community.

- Scope of Practice: Never store, handle, or administer the client's medicine. Unless you are a medical professional and that is in your scope of practice, handling medicine is definitely outside of the psychotherapist's scope. Some practitioners take clients' blood pressure (BP) before medicine sessions, since ketamine can raise blood pressure. If the client's BP is not within normal range, they do not provide the KAP session that day. For me, this is practicing outside of my scope. I am not a medical provider and do not engage in medical assessment. If the prescriber has concerns about a client's blood pressure as relates to ketamine, I do not work with them. I refer them to infusion centers or to other providers staffed by medical personnel.

- Malpractice Insurance: Obtain KAP-specific malpractice insurance. Your insurance may already cover you, but get it in writing. It will stipulate that you are only covered for activities in your scope of practice, namely: psychotherapy. KAP does not ask of the psychotherapist to ever step out of their role as a psychotherapist into another role, specifically that of medical provider.

- Emergency Plans: Outpatient psychotherapists, particularly those in private practices outside of group settings, benefit from a plan about what they would do in an emergency of any sort related to any of our clients. My plan is the same I would use in any emergency in my life, professional or personal: stay calm, assess the situation, call 911 if needed.

RISK OF MISUSE AND ADDICTION

While not an inherently addictive substance, ketamine produces pleasurable effects, making it a risk for recreational use, misuse, abuse and even addiction. It is imperative we have our eye on these risks for our clients.

It is also imperative we have some clarity inside ourselves about our thoughts/feelings/reactions to the use of mood- and mind-altering substances by others.

Drug use is something we as clinicians can get pretty squirrelly about. We have opinions/concerns/theories about what healthy/reasonable/concerning use looks like, which can be influenced by our own use/misuse. We might, for instance feel very differently about a young person's cannabis use versus our evening wine, in which case we are likely to have some reactivity to the risk of unsanctioned ketamine use. Not all our clients are willing, able, nor benefit from keeping ketamine in the collaboratively pre-determined frame built with the therapist. Drug and drug use can be a hot and touchy topic for us and our clients. Even if we think we know our stance well, working with clients around ketamine will test that stance.

Abuse Concerns

Some of our clients might seek to use this medicine outside the boundaries we have defined as our KAP work. Some clinicians attempt to control for this, for instance by requiring the client to bring their prescription into the office routinely to ensure none was taken separately from agreed-upon KAP sessions. If the client takes the medicine outside of their agreement, we may stop doing KAP altogether with the client, or design other protocols to restrict use.

As a general stance, I am not married to the protocol I establish with my client, and definitely not quick to call "unsanctioned" use as abuse, misuse, or otherwise problematic. A friend of mine in the cannabis industry has talked about the industry's rejection of a binary of medical versus recreational, arguing that distinction may be difficult to assess in real time. While my client and I plot and refine our plans for their KAP work, I also trust my client and their own agency. Abuse and addiction are not the only reasons the client may want to explore the medicine outside of our planned sessions; their inner healer and unconscious self may also pull them to the psychedelic journey so that may do their inner work.

I had a client who described her medicine sessions as her "happy place," which scared me a bit and put me on high alert. She was using the medicine almost every other day, which is not an unheard-of protocol, but not the one we had set together. She visited this "happy place" multiple times a week for well over a month. And in her "happy place," she filled herself with enough self-love and goodness to enter therapy with more authority, self-direction, and agency. I would not have built that protocol with her, but it was indeed profoundly healing.

Clients commonly misrepresent and underrepresent many activities they imagine we judge, that they judge about themselves, or that they are attempting to shift/regulate. That may be drug and alcohol use, masturbation and porn, sleeping and TV watching, eating and eating disorder symptoms, picking, hand washing and other obsessive compulsive symptoms, yelling at their kids or name-calling their partners. Efforts to police my clients' activities risks access to what is happening in their lives, what they are struggling with, with themselves and others. That is where all the data is that I need to help them. The safer they can feel to offer up the truths of their struggle, the better I can do my job, which is to be available to think creatively and symbolically about what they are doing and why they might be doing it.

We must remember when working with highly stigmatized medicines, which in my opinion even still includes medical marijuana, to make sure we are creating space in our own minds for original thought as opposed to falling into default-mode thinking. It is also true that if I see my client making consistent improper use of the medicine, or even if KAP is simply failing as a productive mode of treatment, I would not support my client in getting further prescriptions. In my own clinician/prescriber relationship, clients' requests for refills are made in collaboration with the KAP therapist. The most substantial protection against abuse of this medicine I can offer my clients is the collaborative relationship with their prescriber.

Active Addict

There is some compelling research happening with many psychedelics, including ketamine, using these medicines as an intervention in addiction with various substances. The results are hugely significant and promising.

I frequently work with high-functioning, active addicts and others concerned about their substance use, who hope that ketamine and KAP might be helpful for decreasing their reliance on substances. That is quite distinct from someone who reaches out for KAP for the primary purpose of addressing a drug use/misuse/addiction concern. I would do them the courtesy of referring them to an expert in ketamine/KAP-related protocols for addiction. I do not bring the kind of expertise, developed protocols, and supplemental resources that these compelling research studies can offer their subjects, or that some more specifically qualified practitioners may have in abundance. If a potential client comes to me in the grips of a debilitating addiction, I would connect them with someone with addiction-specific protocols and expertise.

For the higher-functioning client interested in using this medicine to think about and explore their relationships to drugs and alcohol, there are a couple safeguards I have in place. If my client was not equally interested in safeguards to protect them from addiction, that would signal me to not provide KAP to the client.

- Local Prescriber Only: For anyone with drug or alcohol use concerns, I would only work with a local prescriber who knew about their drug addiction/abuse/misuse, and for instance, might limit the number of initial doses while we figured out if ketamine is a useful treatment.

- Extended Preparation: Additional sessions would be required to help both client and therapist identify client-specific warning signs that this treatment is too risky, has increased drug and substance use, or has otherwise derailed.

- Rigorous Honesty: We need clients to try to trust us with the gritty details of how their drug and alcohol and ketamine use is going. Here is where we really need to manage some of our own anxiety as they explore the use of this medicine. Again, it may look sloppy and disorganized, confusing for both you and the client, and hard to see the forest (path) for the trees.

Recovering Addict

The current available data on recovering addicts and psychedelics is still quite limited. Many practitioners have primarily positive anecdotal experiences of clients being able to use this medicine within a KAP frame and not returning to active addiction. I am open to providing KAP to some recovering addicts based on an extensive, thorough risk/benefit analysis with the client and any other members of their clinical team.

This client would have an extended evaluation period to assess additional variables related to risk, strength of their current recovery, plans for accessing needed support in case their recovery becomes compromised, assessment of their recovery support system, etc. I would only work with a client actively engaged in therapy, with me or their therapist, for at least a few months on either side of the KAP work for added protection.

We are asking the recovering addict for rigorous honesty about what they have to lose versus what they have to gain before embarking on KAP. Our part of this rigorous honesty is making sure we are clear about and realistic KAP expectations, least idealization of the hopes and dreams of psychedelic-assisted psychotherapy undeservedly tip the scales away from to risk.

A Novel Tool

KETAMINE HOLDS A CANDLE HIGH TO THE OTHER PSYCHEDELICS

Multiple psychedelics are currently in late-stage trials through the FDA as well as some of the country's most prestigious medical research organizations to assess their use in psychedelic-assisted psychotherapy. MDMA, colloquially referred to as ecstasy or molly, is slated for legal use with specially trained psychotherapists as early as 2024. Psilocybin will likely be available for use with similarly trained psychotherapists by 2025. Each medicine offers unique benefits in aiding with various psychological and emotional distress, conundrums, and diagnoses that bring folx into psychotherapy.

Some people eager to explore the way psychedelics might help with their psychotherapy journeys are waiting for these medicines to become available, imagining they are the gold standard. While the medicines will certainly offer unique opportunities, ketamine offers unique features, making it particularly relevant for use as a tool for psychotherapy.

UPSIDES TO KETAMINE

- It is currently legal and available for use in clinical settings, with the medicine itself reasonably priced and accessible through a psychiatrist.

- It is long established as a particularly safe drug with minimal risks and side effects and few clinical or medical contraindications.

- The molecule itself can help with mood disorders, much like standard antidepressants and anti-anxiety medications, but they operate on a different system (glutamate).

- The medicine facilitates neuroplasticity for some days after each treatment, meaning it helps the mind operate outside of its default-mode functioning, creating novel opportunities for growth and change with one's most entrenched thoughts and behaviors.

- The ketamine psychedelic experience only lasts around 40 to 60 minutes, which makes it ideal for first-time psychedelic users or otherwise anxious/nervous/apprehensive clients. The short duration also supports a focused experience, with a sole goal or intention, a handful of thoughts/feelings/experiences, making it easier to harness them for psychotherapeutic aims.

- Because the trip is short in duration, more people can afford to have a therapist present during the experience.

- The medicine has specific features supportive of therapeutic endeavors:

  » It is dissociative. Much like a lucid dream, there is a dreamer and a conscious self who is aware of the dream. The conscious self, like an observing ego, can help direct the dream, think about the dream in real time, and feel some distance from the dream. Even if the dream has some dark or scary elements, there is a conscious self that is separate enough from the experience to provide a feeling of containment and support to the dreamer.

  » The medicine is also an anesthetic, which provides the body with a somatic experience of relaxation, well-being, and containment.

Ketamine is perceived as the ugly step-sister of the psychedelic world. With all the buzz around plant-based medicine, and the allure of the "love-drug truth serum" MDMA, some clients will want to wait for these medicines to become available. While this goal is understandable, ketamine is particularly psychotherapy-user-friendly right now.

KETAMINE IS THE SHORTCUT WE ALL DESERVE

A frequent criticism leveraged against using psychedelics for therapeutic work, efforts toward enlightenment, spiritual connection, and meditative practices, is that it is a shortcut. The implication is that shortcuts are bad—and that, essentially, we only deserve good things if we spend decades of herculean effort to achieve them.

Some people get to live early adult lives with regulated emotional systems, solid self-esteem, and a belief in the general goodness of the world and its ability to meet their basic needs. They get that from good-enough parents who love them sufficiently, with a stable-enough home situation that is free from significant trauma. That is really fabulous, and what we all hope to provide for our own children.

Most of us, however, enter adult life with internal and external barriers to a fully functioning self, with some dark shadows we maneuver to pull off daily life. We may be happy and successful but still have to work with parts of ourselves that are injured and damaged, self-sabotaging, plagued with doubts and mistrust, and all the other ways life can feel complicated and difficult.

As a clinician, the things I hope to help clients minimize, over time, is the stuff they do to relieve their suffering that ultimately hurts them or keeps them in the same stuck place. Most of us do a fair amount of stuff like that, and while not our best move, it may alleviate enough suffering that we should give ourselves a break while we do our work to create new options.

Using ketamine within an assisted psychotherapy experience is not a Band-Aid to alleviate a moment of suffering. It is an activity that has the potential of offering a life-altering experience. The experiences vary widely, and in intensity, but they frequently give people access to new perspectives, narratives, truths, and clarities about themselves, their lives, their relationships, and their world. These experiences are often accompanied by feelings of connectedness, goodness, and well-being. For many, their psychedelic experiences are peak life experiences that become core memories that direct future actions.

Ketamine doesn't solve anything. No one takes it and becomes a new person who has magically resolved their life issues. If it did, it wouldn't have to happen within a therapy context. People would just be better. It provides an experience that the client then needs to use to continue to do the work of self/life/relationship improvement. But what it can offer is a moment of revelation, an epiphany, an embodied somatic experience of goodness. This offers our client inspiration and a vision for the path their self-work can take.

Framing inspiration as an indulgent shortcut is a cynical, cruel, and primitive understanding of what it takes to self-actualize. For any who have been on a journey to self-enlightenment, working to craft a more sustainable, joy-filed life, shortcuts are a welcome opportunity.

KETAMINE IS A THERAPIST'S PLAYGROUND

Part of assessing if a client is a good candidate for ketamine-assisted psychotherapy is sussing out how familiar they are with their own core themes. Ketamine is rarely a well-suited vehicle for those early in their psychotherapy work. Psychedelic therapies in large part are meant to help people get access to unconscious material. Familiarity with the terrain of their unconscious is what allows them to understand the material that surfaces in a medicine session. This makes therapists particularly great candidates for using ketamine as a tool in their own healing.

For therapists deeply familiar with both our unconscious material as well as the unconscious landscape, psychedelics offer a wonderland. Whatever developmental and treatment frameworks we use to understand our clients and our work will symbolically appear in our personal medicine sessions. As an object relations person, I can bump up against my own theoretical structures, confronting my own Kleinian good breast/bad breast and part objects, have a somatic experience of Bion's container and contained concepts, and formulate my own symbols of Winnicott's good-enough mother. My unconscious can serve up my material within these multi-layered concepts.

My own medicine sessions have been both a tool for understanding myself better, but also my theoretical frame. I have come to a deeper understanding, a more embodied and somatic comprehension of my theoretical framework. My sessions have radically enriched my understanding of my internal world, using my theoretical concepts to walk me through complex, dense, core elements of my psyche. Because ketamine produces an effect of dissociation, creating both a dreamer and an observing ego, I am able to influence my dream and ask myself to consider concepts like whether I am facing Bion's failure of an adequate container, or if the issue is an oversized element to be contained. I can explore maternal introjections and tangle apart projective identifications. I can see symbolic representation of material I have failed to sufficiently metabolize. For me, a veritable playground.

PART FIVE

RESOURCES

While hardly comprehensive, this section offers a collection of resources to help start a ketamine-assisted psychotherapy practice. You can find PDFs of these material and other professional KAP resources here.*

Many practitioners are generously open to sharing screening and onboarding tools, educational materials they customarily share with clients and their treatment teams, and all the many resources available to support us in our work. Finding other KAP practitioners is your best bet for curating your collection of resources.

---

* https://fullliving.com/clinical-resources/

Initial Interest Email Correspondence

W hen a new client reaches out for KAP-specific treatment, I start with an email laying out first steps in the process, attaching an evaluation to determine candidacy, a short video explaining the ways ketamine can be a useful tool for therapy, and the following articles. I am offering these up as both examples of the types of materials you might provide clients or as resources that you share with clients.

THREE WAYS KETAMINE CAN HELP

Ketamine is currently legal and available for use as an off-label medication for mental health and mood disorders. It provides three distinct vehicles for possible transformation, each uniquely potent in its own right. These can work separately and in tandem with each other.

The Molecule/Medicine

When administered with a specific protocol, commonly two times a week, for four to six weeks, followed by maybe once every month to three months, the medicine itself can help alleviate symptoms of depression and anxiety. This is particularly promising for folx with chronic mood disorders that have never been significantly helped by other antidepressant or anti-anxiety medication. While expected it will prove to be quite significant for managing mood disorders in lots of folx, the current FDA trials are specific to treatment-resistant depressions. This benefit can be accessed even if the medication is taken at a low dosage that does not induce a psychedelic state.

The Psychedelic Experience

Another way ketamine can be helpful with a wide range of issues is making use of the psychedelic experience to do pieces of therapy work. The medicine provides semi-lucid contact with unconscious material. Whatever therapy themes you are working on, places you feel stuck or confused, questions your have for your unconscious, the psychedelic experience can help access your internal healer, your wiser self.

Some people have what they describe as mystical/spiritual experiences that offer them a radically different perspective on themselves, others, and life itself. Many of us have very narrow world/self/other views that do much to dictate our experience. Psychedelic experiences can often open a totally new understanding.

To make good use of this component, it is best practice to be in an active therapy process or some other super-focused self-improvement/healing activity. The most fruitful medicine journeys are curated through pre-medicine-session intention setting. While the medicine can make a lot happen in the mind/body/experience, we aren't really seeking a random experience, but rather one directed specifically toward our healing. During the medicine session, you have novel neural pathways providing new, original thoughts not burdened by default-mode processing of material. These are opportunities to unravel old, ongoing conundrums. The other reason working with ketamine as a tool for healing is best done in the container of psychotherapy is that the ultimate value of a medicine journey is the successful integration of the material/insight/experience into our daily lives.

Neuroplasticity

The third way ketamine can be helpful is in the days following a session. For three to four days after each medicine session, your mind has serious neuroplasticity. What this means is it is easier for new synaptic connections to occur, and less likely that your thoughts/feelings/behaviors will be forced into the same well-worn groves in your mind that have you stuck in repetition. During the days following treatments, it is important to do lots of journaling, therapy, art, conversations with friends, meditation, walks in the woods, and any new behaviors/thoughts/patterns you hope to establish. This is one of the key ways ketamine can help and must be built into your plans for the days surrounding each treatment if you are to get the most out of this medicine.

WHY KETAMINE AND NOT OTHER PSYCHEDELICS

There are multiple psychedelics currently in late stage trials with the Federal Drug Administration (FDA) and some of the country's most prestigious medical research organizations for use in psychedelic-assisted psychotherapy. MDMA, commonly referred to as ecstasy or molly, is slated for legal use with specially trained psychotherapists in 2024. Psilocybin will likely be ready for use with similarly trained psychotherapies by 2025. They each offer unique benefits in aiding our efforts toward and more fulfilling life.

Some folx eager to explore how these other psychedelics might help are simultaneously reluctant to consider ketamine. As the ugly step-sister of the psychedelics, ketamine doesn't have the mystical allure of plant medicine nor the fond memories many have associated with MDMA. Each psychedelic medicine offers unique properties that lend themselves well to specific functions. Ketamine's unique features make it a particularly excellent medicine to consider for use as a tool for psychotherapy.

Upsides to Ketamine

- **Legal and Available for Use:** It is currently legal and available for use in clinical settings, with the medicine itself reasonably priced and accessible through a prescription.

- **Particularly Safe Medicine:** It has long been established as a particularly safe drug with minimal risks and side effects.

- **Unique Antidepressant Qualities:** The molecule itself can help with mood disorders, much like standard antidepressants and anti-anxiety medications, but operating on a different system (glutamate).

- **Lingering Neuroplasticity:** The medicine facilitates neuroplasticity for days after each treatment, meaning it helps the mind to operate outside of our default-mode functioning, creating novel opportunities for growth and change with our most entrenched thoughts and behaviors.

- **Short Psychedelic Journey:** The psychedelic experience itself only lasts 40 to 60 minutes, which makes it ideal for first-time psychedelic users; allows the medicine session to be focused on a handful of thoughts/feelings/experiences, making it easier to harness/capture them for processing; and also lends itself well to having a therapist present during the shorter experience.

If you are waiting for one of the other medicines for your psychedelic-assisted psychotherapy, reach out for a free 15-minute consultation to see how each medicine aligns with the goals you bring to treatment. It won't be a sales pitch … just an opportunity to think it through with an expert.

WAYS TO ACCESS KETAMINE

Infusion Centers

Infusion centers can be one place to receive ketamine treatment. Eligibility requirements include a history of depression with two previous trials of other antidepressants. For the treatment of treatment-resistant depression, infusions have the most research-tested success as per the molecule itself. Treatment at an infusion center typically requires multiple sessions a seek for several week to experience a decrease in symptoms. Some infusions centers work with some insurance companies, making it a more financially accessible option for some.

Upsides to Infusion Centers:

- Often covered by insurance

- Medical monitoring, which is not necessary for most clients, but can be a comfort to some

- Most tested/documented protocols as successful treatment for the benefits of the molecule itself

Unfortunately, the sessions are less than ideal for a psychedelic experience because of the highly distracting environment, including medical monitoring and chit-chatting staff. Infusion centers are rarely interested in the therapeutic value of the psychedelic journey and are most commonly ill-equip to aid in supporting an environment or process related to the psychedelic experience.

Downsides to Infusion Centers:

- The psychedelic experience can be significantly compromised in the infusion center setting as distractions are at an all time high.

- You will need to have a separate plan for how to prepare for and integrate sessions. Our program can work with you to build a psychotherapy component your work.

- You will need to schedule the sessions, which are time-consuming (about 60 to 90 minutes), two to three times a week during daytime hours and have a means to get to and from the sessions as you cannot drive immediately following a session.

Prescription for Lozenges

Ketamine can be administered multiple ways. Rapid-dissolving or troche lozenges that can then be taken at home or in a psychotherapy setting are most frequently used for ketamine-assisted psychotherapy. These tablets can be self-administered in a location specifically set up for KAP. The setting can be controlled to reduce distractions and increase a sense of containment. At-home or in-office settings allow the participant to have their therapist or another supportive personal available during the medicine sessions themselves.

Psychiatric or Medical Prescriber

Getting a prescription for lozenges can happen in a few ways. If you have a psychiatrist, psychiatric nurse, personal care physician (PCP), nurse practitioner, or physician assistant you already work with, you could discuss it with them to see if they are willing to prescribe ketamine. Truthfully, a lot of folx are still really uncomfortable considering this medication. Having said that, it is worth a discussion with your psychiatric and medical prescribers.

If your own medical provider is not an option, I will connect you with my provider. You will need to meet with them for a virtual session, at a fee of $250, and pay an additional $40 to $70 for the prescription, which can be mailed to your home or picked up at a local compounding pharmacy.

Online Lozenge Providers

There are several online companies that provide evaluations and prescriptions for at-home use, which can then be used with a psychotherapist or for self-directed sessions. Some programs simply offer the medicine; others offer supportive therapy-like services. These tend to be costly but convenient. We can discuss these if they seem like your best option.

VIDEO OVERVIEW OF KAP

Ketamine: A Novel Tool for Our Most Stuck Places
https://youtu.be/ho92jX6wpIk

INTAKE QUESTIONNAIRE KAP

I send this as a google document and use it both to assess candidacy and get authorization for contact with their medical and psychotherapy providers.

First and Last Name
Email Address
Cell Phone #
Date of Birth
City, State, Zip Code

Are you currently working with a psychiatrist or other prescriber for mental health related medications?

If yes, is your psychiatrist or medical prescriber aware of your interest in ketamine treatment?

Do you authorize Full Living to exchange information with your psychiatrist or medical prescriber for purposes of coordinating your treatment?

If yes, please provide your psychiatrist or medical prescriber's name, email address, and phone number.

Have you ever been in psychotherapy?

If yes, how many times, for how long, and at what ages (approximate)?

Are you currently in psychotherapy?

If yes, is your psychotherapist aware of your interest in ketamine treatment?

Do you authorize Full Living to exchange information with your psychotherapist for purposes of coordinating your treatment?

If yes, please provide your psychotherapist's name, email address, and phone number.

Have you ever received a mental health diagnosis?

If yes, please list the diagnosis you have received.

Please check any mental health conditions below you believe may apply to you.

- Bipolar Disorder
- Dissociative Identity Disorder
- Dissociative Disorder
- Schizophrenia
- Schizoaffective Disorder
- Post-Traumatic Stress Disorder
- Psychosis, Psychotic Illness, or Episode
- Mania or Manic Episode

If you checked any of the boxes above, please briefly explain here and be prepared to discuss in our intake session.

Please check any of the life conditions below that may apply to you.

- Experienced Intimate Partner Violence
- Major Surgeries/Procedures Requiring Anesthesia
- Significant Experiences of Trauma
- Hospitalization for Mental Health Condition
- Attempted Suicide
- Current Risk for Self-Harm
- Current Suicidality

If you checked any of the boxes above, please briefly explain here and be prepared to discuss in our intake session.

Please check all medical conditions that may apply to you.

- High Blood Pressure
- Hypertension
- Heart Condition, Irregularity, Instability, Disease
- Allergy to ketamine
- Kidney or Bladder Disease
- Liver Disease
- Hyperthyroidism
- Other
- No history of physical health issues

If you checked any of the boxes above, provide a brief explanation here, including how the condition is currently being treated, and be prepared to discuss in your intake session.

Are you, or might you be pregnant?

Please list all current medications and what conditions they are used to treat.

Please include current alcohol and drug usage, including type and frequency of use.

Please indicate any previous experience with psychedelics, including type and frequency of use.

Please describe any struggles with overuse, addiction, or abuse of any drugs or alcohol, prescription or otherwise.

In your own words, please describe what concerns and goals you hope ketamine treatment will help you to address.

Medicine Session Preparation Packet

After a client is deemed an appropriate candidate for KAP, I send them an email with the following attachments to help them begin to percolate on questions and intentions before our upcoming preparation sessions. This will help us develop a common language for their work.

PREPARING YOURSELF FOR A FRUITFUL EXPERIENCE

Before embarking on medicine sessions with ketamine, it is important to have a plan for making the most of this novel tool for growth and change. While the medicine itself is useful to a significant majority of the people who take ketamine a couple times a week for four to eight weeks, its potential benefits do not end with the molecule itself.

During the medicine session, you will have easy access to unconscious material that holds key information about your core themes. And unlike a dream state, you may well be lucid and have some conscious ability to direct and influence this dream-like state. You will be able to ask yourself questions about your most stuck places and enter a dialogue with your inner healing intelligence.

Set and Setting

In large part what distinguishes psychedelic-assisted psychotherapy from recreational psychedelic use is what is coined "set and setting." Set references the participant's mind**set**, goals, and intentions, and setting is the social and physical environment in which the participant will have their medicine session. Psychedelics, when used thoughtfully, can help induce life-changing experiences.

Establishing intentions prior to a psychedelic experience helps cultivate the right "set" by priming your mind with your treatment objectives, or what you hope to gain or learn from the experience. As much intentionality as you can bring to the session the better. This dramatically increases the likelihood of having a positive, therapeutically valuable experience.

Honing your Intention

Determining the shape of your intention begins by considering what motivated you to seek out psychedelic-assisted therapy. While we often bring many hopes and dreams to new healing opportunities, the more focused you can be about your intentions for a particular medicine session, the more likely you are to get an experience directed at that theme.

An intention can be something broad, such as understanding the root of your depression or anxiety. It can be related to an ongoing event, like how to deal with a significant life loss. It can be related to a wish to shift something in your personality structure, in how you approach yourself, others, and your life. It can also be something ostensibly lighter, such as how to find more joy in your daily routine.

Common themes include:

- Discerning what is in your way/holding you back/interfering with your goals

- Healing from traumas/losses/injury

- Improving your relationship to self/others/life

- Freeing yourself from repetitive thoughts/behaviors

- Cultivating gratitude/joy

Here are some types of questions that might help you determine your intentions:

- What drew you to this tool?

- What were you hoping it would help you with?

- What suffering plagues you?

- Where in your psychic life do you feel you are unable to gain traction?

- What are the stuck places that you find yourself circling around year after year?

- How does your behavior compare to your goals, values, and self-beliefs?

- What would you like to change about your approach to yourself, others, work, your life?

- What holds you back from living the life you want?

Honing your intentions means taking this step seriously. Do some journal writing about what you hope to get from your medicine session, talk with your friends and therapist, meditate, and take walks in the woods. Start to hone the thought into a question that you will be asking your unconscious. The beauty of psychedelic-assisted psychotherapy is that there is no confusion about where your answers lie: not with your therapist, not with your friends, not in a book, but rather in your own inner healing intelligence. It is your own inner healing wisdom to whom you will direct your questions and requests:

- Show me a way out of my depression/anxiety/obsessive compulsive disorder.

- I want an experience of feeling loved.

- Help me understand what's hurting me/why I am stuck.

- How can I access more gratitude/joy/patience/love?

- Who am I with my repetitive thoughts/behaviors/reactions?

- Help me forgive myself.

- Help me find the path to heal from my trauma/loss/sadness?

Other Components of Set

In addition to having a specific intention in mind for your medicine session, there are some other ways to make sure you come to your day of treatment in the best mindset.

In many indigenous cultures, psychedelics are used for all kinds of healing of the body and the mind. But unlike those of us in Western cultures, who take our medicines at home with a glass of water or on our way to work, medicines in the form of psychedelics are taken as part of a sacred act in ceremony. While we may not be able to replicate that level of reverie for the medicine, it behooves us to glean some lessons from these traditions.

In the week prior to your ketamine session, particularly your first one, you might consider treating the upcoming session as an important event that is allowed to occupy your mind throughout the week. You might give yourself opportunities to have it in mind by journaling about it, talking with friends and family, doing some yoga and meditation, going for walks or sitting in nature.

While it doesn't benefit you to make any extreme alterations to your body in the week before your session, some folx try to minimize use of alcohol, cannabis, nicotine, caffeine, or other substances. Some might even decrease consumption of meat and dairy, and perhaps increase their consumption of fresh fruits and vegetables and drink more water. Similarly, it is a great time to increase body-based activity like exercise, but only slightly. This isn't a week for juice cleansing and running marathons: just thoughtful, moderate, self-care.

GUIDEPOSTS FOR YOUR JOURNEY

Prior to your first medicine session, you will have done some work on your own and with your therapist to develop an intention for your session. The specificity of this intention will do a lot to direct your mind where to go and what you want to have happen during your medicine session experience. Having said that, the medicine offers a lot of mental fluidity, and sometimes folx feel like they are getting a little lost in their thoughts and emotions during the session. There are a few tools that are great to know about beforehand, though your sitter will also be there to direct you toward them during the session itself.

Inner Healing Intelligence

One of the exciting elements of psychedelics is the way it provides such pervasive access to unconscious material but while in a lucid state. Unlike dreams, we have a conscious self available during the session that can ask questions and influence the direction of the mind.

One of the exciting elements of psychedelic-assisted psychotherapy is that by design the sitters are trained to be non-directive. Rather than the sitter or therapist suggesting what the client might do, or think, or consider, or interpret, we are trained to direct you to yourself, more specifically, your inner healing wisdom, for your answers. Psychedelic-assisted psychotherapy assumes that you are the best source for the answers to your questions, and that the ketamine will clear out the barriers to using your own wisdom.

What this looks like during the session is using the "term" Inner Healing Intelligence as a mantra, or guidepost, during the session. If you feel lost or uncertain about what is coming up for you or wanting to help your unconscious bring the right material to the surface, you might think or say out loud the words Inner Healing Intelligence. You might ask your intention question, again, in your mind or out loud, saying something like "Inner Healing Intelligence, help me understand how I can free myself of my depression"?

TLO

Trust, Let Go and Be Open. These are the tools for a fruitful trip. There are lots of reasons it can be hard for us to get out of our own way, in life, and in our medicine sessions. While we have set an intention, and have a goal, our inner healing intelligence may have a very different plan for our medicine session. While generally in life, giving over your agency to "another" is rarely advised, your inner healing intelligence isn't another. It is the best of you. It is the seat of your unconscious wisdom. It is the wisest guide for your journey.

If you find yourself nervous, or scared, resistant, or working too hard to direct or control your journey, this is the mantra to help you hand over the journey to the medicine and your inner healing wisdom. Say in your mind or out loud, "trust, let go, be open" over and over, while you take deep breaths.

Deep Breaths

Deep breaths have never felt as good as they do during a medicine session. Even the most skilled mediator would have a hard time accessing the state of deep relaxation the medicine provides. Deep breaths will help you feel connected to your body during the experience and help you feel your way through the session.

WEEK OF/NIGHT OF/DAY OF PREP

Okay, some specific stuff about the next couple days. The best way to engage this medicine is to treat it like an event or a ceremony, so preparation helps.

The Next Few Days

- Read through the two attached articles

- Try to limit/reduce use of cannabis, alcohol, or other drugs

- Do moderate movement … not too much or too little … get a calm flow going

- Eat healthfully, but nothing extreme like fasts or cleanses

- Sleep well

- Spend time in nature

- Meditate and journal some, talk with friends, think about your intentions

Day Before

- Don't do any big indulgences … don't eat too much, or drink too much, or run a marathon, or do a day of silent meditation

- Drink lots of fluids

- Don't drink too much caffeine

- Moderate movement … not too much or too little … get a calm flow going

Day of

- Try not to eat for three hours before the session

- Stop drinking fluids one hour before the session

- Take your anti-nausea medication an hour before the session

- Wear comfy clothes

- Have your journal with you

After Your Medicine Session

- Make sure the person driving you home knows you may or may not want to talk

- Make sure the person you are with after the session knows you might be having novel thoughts neither they nor you have heard before, and that it isn't the time to try to convince you of their theory or perspective... that it is an opportunity for you to explore your own untapped thoughts/perspectives, to be evaluated later

- Don't operate machinery, drive, use knives or the sort until you feel totally in your body

- Drink fluids

FAMILY/FRIEND KETAMINE-ASSISTED PSYCHOTHERAPY (KAP) SUPPORT PERSON

You have someone in your life who has been prescribed ketamine as a tool for improving their mental health. As an unfamiliar and powerful medicine, this document seeks to provide some guidance to those supporting the KAP participant. You may be offering to "sit" for them during a medicine session, drive them to and from a medicine session, or you may just be someone in their life who is likely to see and be impacted by the changes brought about by this novel treatment.

During the Session

- **Group Text with Therapist:** If you are going to be the adult support to the participant's at-home medicine session, you will be in a text group with the participant and the KAP provider prior to the session in case you have questions, concerns, or other reasons you may want to be in active contact with the therapist.

- **Support the Right Setting:** The participant is going to need a quiet, distraction-free place to have the medicine session.

- **What to Expect:** The participant is going to take the medicine by mouth. It will take 15 to 40 minutes for the medicine to take effect. They will be lying down, with an eye mask, and unlikely to talk or move much for the main part of the medicine session, which typically lasts between 20 to 60 minutes.

- **Checking in on Participant:** Depending on what you and the participant agree to, you may stay in the room where they are having the session, or in another room nearby. If you are not in the same room with them, you will need to come in to check on them every 30 minutes. Depending on what you two agree, it may be a silent visit, or you might ask them if they need anything. They may have difficulty hearing or answering, which is not a sign that anything is wrong.

- **Bathroom Support:** One thing they may need is to go to the bathroom. If that is the case, it is good for you to physically support them in getting to and from the bathroom.

- **Not a Time for Conversation:** The participant may be interested in talking during the medicine session. Truthfully, it is a bit ill advised. The main purpose of the medicine is to commune with the self, so as much as you feel able, it is good to direct the participant to their internal world, saying things like, "Why don't you ask yourself that question?" or "I wonder what other thoughts you have about that?" or "Why don't you lean into that thought/feeling/question?" You might also offer basic reassurance, like, "I am here," "You are safe," You are doing the brave thing."

Immediately Following the Session

- **Unsafe to Drive:** Because the medicine acts as an anesthetic, the participant will not be safe to drive immediately following medicine sessions. If they are receiving their treatment at an infusion center, therapist's office, or retreat location of sort, they will need to be driven home.

- **Temporary Impairment:** The participant may be groggy, mentally, and physically impaired immediately following treatment. They may need support walking, getting in and out of vehicles, or using a restroom.

- **Follow Their Lead:** The medicine often provides a powerful experience, a "trip," much like a lucid dream. After the medicine session, the participant is likely to still be deep in thought. They may or may not want to talk. They may or may not want to eat. They may or may not want to sleep. The support person can be of best use by following the participant's lead and helping the participant decide what they need.

- **New Ideas:** Immediately following medicine sessions, the participant may still be in a bit of a dream state. Their brain is fluid, covering new territory, coming up with new thoughts and associations. Sometimes these are profound connections that help the participant gain a new understanding of themselves, but until they are digested in the days and weeks following a session, they are still just thoughts/considerations. If the participant wants to talk about their experience, that is great, and the things they say may be gems, but they should not be treated by the support person as facts or ultimate truths until the participant has fully digested them. It is an important time to avoid initiating topics for conversation, getting into any conflict, challenging their thoughts or ideas. It is an

important time for them to be allowed to be quiet and contem-
plative, or to be allowed to talk about their experience in a solely
self-directed way.

- **Low-Key Plan:** The participant should be supported/encouraged
to reduce distractions and overstimulation in the hour or so proceeding a session. It isn't a great time to go to a party, have dinner
with friends, watch TV, or return to work. It is a time for some
quiet, mellow activities, like talking, writing, listening to music,
relaxing, or even sleeping.

- **Be Non-Directive:** Some of the beauty of the medicine is that it
allows participants to connect to their unconscious and inner healer.
During the medicine session itself, and the hours or so following it,
it is best that the participant's thoughts take center stage. It is not
the best time to try to insert our thoughts/theories/beliefs/priorities.

In the Days/Weeks Proceeding the Treatment

- **Hopes for Big Change:** The participant has decided to engage in
ketamine-assisted psychotherapy because they are hoping to make
some significant shift in their lives/mood/perspective/relationships/
self/world-view.

- **Change May Look Different:** While most of us agree that we would
want the people in our lives to be happier and healthier, sometimes
that looks different than we imagined and has consequences we
might have mixed feelings about.

- **Big Change Destabilizes Intimate Others:** When an intimate other
changes, so do their relationships with us, their expectations, and
perspective on what/who/how they want in their lives. This can be
scary or uncomfortable, and we may want to resist the changes they
are hoping to make for themselves and their lives.

- **Big Change Requires Time for Reflection:** Participants are discouraged from making big changes early in their KAP treatment for the obvious reason that even big realizations need time to digest and metabolize before getting played in our lives. For instance, if early in someone's treatment they wanted to get divorced, move, quit their job, or have a new child, their therapist would discourage them from doing so reactively.

- **Big Change was the Goal:** It is also true though that the medicine can provide big epiphanies and clarities. For instance, the participant might realize there is a dynamic in one of their intimate relationships that is no longer tolerable and that they want that shifted immediately. Remember that they are seeking to free themselves from the things that burden them.

- **Bottom Line:** Ketamine can successfully speed up someone's efforts to heal and grow. Good time to buckle up!

Professional Resources

n this rapidly expanding field, there are some great resources available for clinicians as we begin this work, but also to support us throughout our careers. Here are a handful of resources:

BIG TENT KETAMINE

Big Tent Ketamine is a discussion group for all things related to the therapeutic, intentional use of ketamine in the service of the mental and psycho-spiritual health of individuals, communities, and the planet. It is intended to be a safe space for all providers to discuss matters directly and indirectly related to this work.

Membership is open to prescribers (irrespective of their core specialty), non-prescribing therapists, pharmacists, researchers, and others who work with ketamine. You must be actively licensed, or a post-graduate actively working toward licensure to be eligible to join the group. To join the *Big Tent Ketamine* listserv, send an email to Carl Spitzer, MD: carl.spitzer@gmail.com.

KETAMINE RESEARCH FOUNDATION

The Ketamine Research Foundation is the world's leading information resource on ketamine with over 5,000 titles with full-text references, powerful new search functions, and a highly optimized user experience.

The library is online at https://ketamineresearchfoundation.org/library/. Public access to the library's full research collection is available through the nonprofit Ketamine Research Foundation for $100 per year. The Ketamine Library is a complete reference source for researchers and laypeople interested in ketamine in all its aspects. For more information, please visit https://ketamineresearchfoundation.org/.

POPULAR GUIDED MEDITATION

There are many creative and productive ways to spend the moments immediately before administration of the medication. Whether doing sessions at home, in our outpatient offices, at an infusion center, or a retreat setting, the moments before medicine administration, and as the medicine is taking effect, are great times to be very intentional about cultivating the energy of the medicine session. Poems, meditation and breathing exercises, music, rituals, and movement can all be used to facilitate a generative mindset. Many folx in the field like to read a variation on this meditation as the client is settling into the medicine session. I have seen many versions of these instructions, tweaked by clinicians to align with their particular framework. Here is a version for your own edits and additions:

KAP Flight Instructions/Orientation to the Journey

You are at the start of a journey. Every journey has a beginning, middle, and an end. Wherever you go, you will come back. Try to approach the journey with curiosity, like an anthropologist, archeologist, explorer of new and old worlds.

Lean into trusting the process, the medicine, your own inner healing intelligence, and our therapy relationship. I am here to support you and I invite you to rest into that support. You can tell me what you need to feel comfortable and I will do my best to respond.

Relax your critical mind, follow the medicine's effects and your own inner healing intelligence. Sometimes the body wants to release in tears, sounds, or movements. Let it.

If something beautiful or magical emerges, you can move toward it, connect with it, allow yourself to melt into it; if something is challenging, scary, confusing, or disturbing, in a similar way, you can move toward it with curiosity and inquiry. You can ask what it is there to teach you and/or to show you. Trust that whatever comes up in a session needs to come up even if you do not fully understand it. We will have plenty of time to unpack it all over the coming weeks.

You do not need to feel pressure to talk or to respond to any verbal invitations. This is your time, for your needs. You can ask for help whenever you need it and I will do my best to support you.

Note: This is meant to be read to the client, after they have swirled and either spit out or swallowed the medicine, are lying down with their eye masks on, getting ready for their journey.

Consents For Treatment

KAP providers have created a plethora of models for various consents for KAP treatment. Outside of official guidelines and protocols outlined for our practice, some practitioners have consulted lawyers exploring different priorities, concerns, and policies. The good news is that many practitioners are willing to share their documents with our growing professional community to help us crowd-source options for consent forms for your practice.

My forms tend to prioritize clear communication with clients. What that means is they make less use of legal language, and therefore may have less standing in court should that ever be required. Feel free to use or adapt based on your own needs, practice policies, and priorities.

GENERAL CONSENT FOR KETAMINE-ASSISTED PSYCHOTHERAPY

_____ I understand that when ketamine is taken once or twice a week for four to six weeks, it can help reduce symptoms of depression in two-thirds of people who follow this protocol. One-third do not experience symptom relief from the medicine.

_____ I understand ketamine offers mental neuroplasticity for three to four days after taking the medicine, facilitating new thoughts and opportunities for a new narrative, making the days following each treatment an important time for journaling, conversation, meditation, and efforts to build new habits.

_____ I understand that during the medicine session, I will be sedated by the medicine, lying down, using eye shades, with my KAP provider by my side. Depending on the dosage and its effect on me, I will either be in a deeply relaxed state or will enter into a psychedelic state of lucid dreaming. I may experience it as difficult to move or speak during parts of the medicine session. Typically the effect of the medicine lasts 40 to 60 minutes.

_____ I understand that it may take a few medicine sessions to acquire the right dose in order to experience a psychedelic state. This medicine has multiple ways it can be effective as a treatment tool for many psychological/emotional/mental/mood/spiritual goals, and can be impactful with or without a psychedelic effect.

_____ I understand that following the most intense part of the medicine session, I may still feel a bit sedated, be less than steady on my feet, have slightly blurred vision, experience some dizziness, nausea, dry mouth, restlessness, impaired coordination and concentration, and headache.

_____ I understand that some people experience nausea during or after the medicine session and that my prescriber will also prescribe an anti-nausea medicine that I will take an hour before my medicine session.

_____ I understand that my KAP provider does not prescribe ketamine or other medications. I will secure my prescription through a legal medical provider and will show proof of that prescription before proceeding with medicine sessions with my KAP provider.

_____ I understand that ketamine is a safe medicine, familiar to the medical community, and is being prescribed as an off-label use for mood. I have been cleared for use of this medicine by my prescriber and have discussed any medical concerns with them during my medical consultation.

_____ I understand that for any medicine sessions conducted live with my KAP provider, I will need to arrange safe transportation home and I will not be able to drive, walk, or take public transportation immediately after the medicine session.

_____ I understand that if I intend to do medicine sessions at home, I have signed an additional consent form outlining those requirements.

_____ I understand that if my KAP provider has offered therapeutic touch as part of the medicine session, I have signed an additional consent outlining those requirements.

_____ I understand that the use of ketamine is not a requirement of my psychotherapy work but rather a particular tool I am interested in exploring.

_____ I have been given sufficient opportunities to explore my questions and concerns regarding this treatment tool and do not feel rushed by the KAP provider to begin ketamine-assisted psychotherapy.

_____

Client Name

_____

Client Signature   Date

_____

Therapist Name

_____

Therapist Signature   Date

KAP CONSENT: THERAPEUTIC TOUCH

This consent form covers the agreement between the client and KAP provider(s) listed below, and no other persons present during the KAP medicine session. There may be other instances of incidental touch, such as helping the client walk or steady themselves, provided by other assistants in the clinical setting. This consent covers intentional therapeutic touch.

_____ I have discussed the option of being offered touch during my psychedelic session and have decided I do/do not want to be touched during the session.

_____ I understand if I have said I do not want to be touched I cannot change my mind for the current session during the session.

_____ I understand that if I have said I do want to be offered touch during my session, I can change my mind at any time and those wishes will be honored.

_____ I have participated in a touch-refusal exercise to practice saying I do not want to be touched.

The ways I have communicated that I do and do not want to be touched are reflected below. (Examples include the therapist holding your hand, holding your feet, laying their hands on your head or arm)

_____

_____

_____

_____

Name of Client

_____

Signature   Date

_____

Name of KAP Provider

_____

Signature   Date

_____

Name of Additional KAP Provider

_____

Signature   Date

_____

Name of Witness

_____

Signature   Date

AT-HOME KAP CONSENT (SITTER/DOSAGE/CONTACT)

The following are requirements for your participation in at-home ketamine use as part of your ketamine-assisted psychotherapy.

- During each session, you will have a responsible adult, "sitter," in the environment.
  - » Provide them with the sitter education form
  - » They can be in the room with you, or another room.
  - » They will need to check in on you every 30 minutes.
  - » The therapist and sitter will be in text or phone contact at the start of each of your medicine sessions.
    - – The therapist is available for any questions or concerns you or your sitter might have throughout the duration of the medicine session.
- At the start of each medicine session, you will be in touch with your KAP therapist.
  - » You will report your dosage
  - » You will discuss your intention

_____

Client Name

_____

Client Signature   Date

_____

Therapist Name

_____

Therapist Signature   Date

ACKNOWLEDGMENTS

I have a small family of origin, and years of effort and flexibility and generosity from each of us has harvested very loving, supportive, and centrally important relationships. To my sister and my dad, I thank you for always staying on the journey no matter how rocky or uncertain our many terrains. The quality of our current relationships is one of my life's greatest treasures.

Friends and community have always been central to how I populate a rich life. In good times or bad, friendships are one of the pillars on which I build the structure of my life. I would be forever at sea in my own mind and soma without them. My friends tirelessly support my efforts to understand my own journey as a human, parent, partner, friend, daughter, therapist, sister, citizen, and my next obsession of unfolding into an aging crone.

For my professional brainstorming, my regulars are also my nearest and dearest: Carrie Askin, Kay Mesh, Tina DiSanto, Susan Schewel, and Kendra Martin. I love to talk business with you gals!

I wasn't sure if I was going to tiptoe into the KAP world or jump in. Reconnecting with a former colleague, Sophia Brandstetter in the KAP world set the stage for one of my favorite professional collaborations and collaborators of all time. We are both tickled to have found a competent, enthusiastic, like-minded clinician and business partner for our many future ventures, but I argue I got the better deal. Thank you so much for keeping me excited and inspired, dividing and conquering tasks, laughing and venting and keeping each other grounded. Well, and for help with tech. Obviously thank you for that.

In an analytic tradition that names its great teachers, even when the frame for teaching was the therapy itself, I owe an immeasurable amount of gratitude to my own therapist, Charles Ashbach. You have traveled with me on countless harrowing and heart-healing journeys. My life has been made infinitely richer on your couch, in your reverie.

I am not sure how to capture the profound gratitude I feel toward my clients over the decades of my work, without falling into some absurd trope. But really, what a way to spend a life, to be allowed to sit with people as they do the sacred work of facing and holding their truths. May we continue to inspire each other to be very brave.

.

Made in the USA
Las Vegas, NV
22 December 2023

83261715R10095